Book A

Maths Exercises for GCSE

Book A

Maths Exercises for GCSE

Philip Holt

Head of Mathematics, Wimbledon College, London

Nelson

Thomas Nelson and Sons Ltd
Nelson House   Mayfield Road
Walton-on-Thames   Surrey
KT12 5PL   UK

51 York Place
Edinburgh
EH1 3JD   UK

Thomas Nelson (Hong Kong) Ltd
Toppan Building 10/F
22A Westlands Road
Quarry Bay   Hong Kong

Distributed in Australia by

Thomas Nelson Australia
480 La Trobe Street
Melbourne   Victoria 3000
and in Sydney, Brisbane, Adelaide and Perth

© Philip Holt, 1988
First published by Thomas Nelson and Sons Ltd 1988
ISBN 0–17–431045–5
NPN 987654321
Printed and bound in Great Britain by
Thomson Litho Ltd, East Kilbride, Scotland

Credits for photographs in this volume are due to the following: All-Sport, Fig 6.5 and
Fig 24.1a; Chris Ridgers Photography for all other photographs.
Cover photograph: The Photo Source.

Preface

This is the first of two books which are designed to provide practice at questions of the type likely to appear in GCSE Mathematics examinations. The book does not attempt to cover the new coursework techniques of problem solving and investigations.

All the GCSE examining groups allow the mathematics examination to be taken at three overlapping levels. In these books I have followed the Southern Examining Group by using the terms *Level 1*, *Level 2* and *Level 3* to describe the lower, intermediate and higher levels. The present book is suitable for Level 1 students and for those who are either clearly Level 2 or on the borderline between Levels 1 and 2, while the second book will cater for Levels 2 and 3 in a similar way. Both books are designed to be used in the final year or eighteen months of a GCSE course, when many students will have completed the syllabus and need revision together with practice at examination questions.

The main exercises are set out in pairs (1A, 1B; 2A, 2B; etc.), which cover the same material and are of roughly equal length and difficulty. Thus the first member of the pair might be used for classwork or teacher exposition and the second for homework. The book also contains a few 'quick revision' exercises, mainly to provide practice in the more important basic techniques such as the manipulations of fractions, decimals and percentages. Each quick revision exercise is placed just before the pair of GCSE exercises in which the techniques it covers are required.

Certain of the topics and exercises are described in the book as *Level 2*. This means that they are required *only* for Level 2 examinations and are therefore unsuitable, on the whole, for Level 1 students. There are, of course, minor differences in the syllabuses of the various examining groups, and some judgements must be applied by teachers regarding the questions which are appropriate for their particular students. The other exercises, which form the majority of the book, are suitable for both levels, though the questions vary in difficulty and it should not be thought that every student needs or will be able to attempt every question. Indeed, few students would have the time to work through the entire book. My hope is that at least half of the questions in each of the main exercises will be suitable for any particular student.

At the end of the book three 'GCSE papers' are provided. These consist entirely of questions taken from the specimen papers issued by the four English examining groups.

Philip Holt
1988

Contents

Everyday arithmetic

Numbers

Relationships between numbers, directed numbers

Inequality symbols and brackets (Level 2)

Types of numbers

Natural numbers, rational and irrational numbers, common factors and multiples (Level 2)

Number patterns and sequences

Fractions and Decimals

Percentage

Further percentage (Level 2)

Units, Measurement, Estimation

Decimal places, significant figures (Level 2)

Indices, Standard Form (Level 2)

Time

Ratio and Proportion

Rate

Graphs

Statistics

Probability

Algebra

Mensuration

Geometry

Trigonometry, Pythagoras' Theorem (Level 2)

GCSE Specimen Papers

Everyday Arithmetic

1   A party for 30 young children is planned at the local Community Centre hall. The costs are as follows:

Hall	£10 an hour
Conjurer	£8 an hour
Food	70p per child
Prizes	£16

The hall is hired for $3\frac{1}{2}$ hours and the conjurer is engaged for $1\frac{1}{4}$ hours.
    a Work out the total cost of putting on the party.

The parents contribute £2.50 for each child and the Community Centre pays the remaining expenses.

    b Work out how much the Community Centre pays.

2   In a town with 23 100 voters, 11 900 vote Conservative at the General Election and the Conservatives have a majority over Labour of 3400 votes.
    a How many people vote Labour?
    b How many people vote neither Conservative nor Labour?

3   An article is offered in a shop at £3.97. If you pay for it with a £10 note, how much change will you get?

4   A clothes shop displays the notice on the left.
    a In June, Ravi decides he would like to buy a jacket marked at £34. How much will he save by waiting and buying it in the sale?
    b On 2 July, Sally buys a jumper which has been reduced by £1.20. What was its original price and how much does Sally actually pay?

5   A grocer buys apples in boxes of 25.
    a How many boxes must she buy if she needs 350 apples?
    b If she needs 135 apples, how many boxes must she buy and how many unwanted apples will she get?

6   To get to her aunt's house, Wanda has to travel 35 miles by train, 5 miles by bus and walk 1 mile.
    a How far does Wanda travel in 4 visits (there and back) to her aunt?
    b In how many visits does Wanda travel 560 miles by public transport?

7   A garden centre displays the notice on the left.
    If the plants are bought as cheaply as possible, what is the cost of:
    a 12 plants?   b 29 plants?   c 48 plants?

8   Mr Smith, Mr Murphy and Mr Singh all have jobs which give them a fixed weekly wage. Mr Smith earns £1028 in 13 weeks, Mr Murphy earns £748 in 9 weeks and Mr Singh earns £824 in 10 weeks. Which man has the highest wage?

Willow
Garden Centre

Buy your bedding plants here
14p each OR
50p for a box of 5

9   In snooker, 1 point is given for potting a red ball, 6 points for potting a pink ball and 7 points for potting a black ball.
    a How many points are scored by potting 7 reds, 2 pinks and 5 blacks?
    b A player scores 59 points by potting 17 balls, all of which are reds, pinks or blacks. Given that 9 of the balls are reds, how many of them are blacks?

10 The following table shows single train fares for adults. Children travel half-price.

London

£17.50	Chester		
£12	£16	Bath	
£8.50	£19	£16	Dover

    a How much would it cost a man and his wife to travel from Chester to Dover?

    A child travels from Dover to London, stays overnight and then goes on to Bath. Find

    b the total fare paid,
    c the amount the child would save by travelling from Dover to Bath direct.

11 A chess club charges an annual subscription of £15, and a fee of 30p each time a player represents the club in a match.
    a How much does a man pay who stays at the club for 4 years and plays for the club 12 times?
    b A woman pays £34.50 for a 2-year period at the club. How many matches does she play in?

12 A shop stocks four types of pencil, which cost 11p, 13p, 15p and 17p.
    a A teacher buys a set of pencils, all of the same type, and gets 9p change from £4. Which type does she buy and how many does she obtain?
    b Another teacher also has £4 to spend, and wants to use as much of it as possible in buying one type of pencil. Which type should he choose in order to get the minimum possible change?
    c Find all the possible ways of buying exactly two types of pencil and spending exactly £1.

Exercise 1B

1   A cricketer sets out to make at least 200 runs in his next four innings. If he scores 15, 78 and 39 in his next three innings, how many does he need to score in his fourth?

2   The same bags of tea are sold by three different shops in the boxes shown on the left.

    Which of the three is the best buy?

3   How many 13p stamps can I get for £2, and how much change will I receive?

4 In a sale, the price of towels is cut from £5.75 to £4.99. How much does a man save by buying 4 towels in the sale?

5 Rita Kelly takes part in a sponsored swim for cancer research. The following diagram shows the first few lines of her sponsorship form.

CANCER RESEARCH SPONSORED SWIM		
Name of sponsor	Amount paid per length	Total paid
Mrs T. Kelly	15p	£2.40
MR T. KELLY	30p	
Bill Jones	5p	
Jan S.	10p	

    a Work out the number of lengths Rita swims and fill in the missing entries in the right-hand column.

    b Rita has been asked to raise £20. In addition to the above sponsors she has an aunt who will probably give 20p per length and some friends who might give 10p per length each. Work out how many of these friends she is likely to need.

6 When an athlete runs once round a track, she covers 380 metres.

    a How far does the athlete run when she does $4\frac{1}{2}$ circuits of the track?

    b How many **complete** circuits must she make to cover more than 5000 metres?

7 A video recorder can be bought for £250 cash, or on credit by putting down a deposit of £25 and paying 12 monthly instalments of £21. How much is saved by paying cash?

8 The following is an order to a mail order clothes firm.
Work out the amounts which should go in the spaces in the right-hand column.

CODE NO.	ITEM	NO. OF ITEMS	PRICE PER ITEM	TOTAL PRICE
M215	Grey mini-skirt	2	£11.46	
W043	White sweatshirt	3	£9.85	
W173	Black denim jacket	1	£17.90	
W258	Black woollen tights	4	£6.37	
Add £1.20 postage for 1-4 items, £1.80 for 5-10 items, £2.40 for more than 10 items.			POSTAGE	
			GRAND TOTAL	

9 Sunita has a part-time job in a pizza restaurant which pays her £4.20 per hour on weekdays. When she works at weekends she gets over-time at 'time and a half'.

   a One week Sunita works 3 hours on Monday, 5 hours on Thursday and 4 hours on Saturday. How much does she earn?

   b Another week Sunita earns £46.20 by working 2 hours on Wednesday, $3\frac{1}{2}$ hours on Saturday and for a certain time on Sunday. Work out this time.

10 A shop sells wall tiles in packs of 6, 9, 15 and 17.

   a I need 100 tiles for my bathroom and decide to buy a set of packs, all of the same size, which will give me 2 spare tiles in case of breakages. Which type do I buy and how many packs do I get?

   b For another job in the kitchen 57 tiles are needed. List all the ways of obtaining exactly this number by buying two pack sizes.

11 A sales person is payed £200 per month and a commission of £36 on each article she sells.

   a How much money does she earn in 3 months if she sells 50 articles in that time?

   b If she normally sells 10 articles per month, how much money can she expect to make in a year?

   c How many articles must she sell in 2 months to make £1300 in that time?

12 When Mike goes to the seaside by train, the return fare is £13.50. He can go more cheaply by coach, but the complete trip then takes 40 minutes longer.

   a If Mike saves £4.20 by going three times (there and back) by coach rather than by train, what is the return coach fare?

   b After a certain number of train trips, Mike calculates that he has saved 4 hours by taking the train rather than the coach. Work out the total cost of these trips.

Numbers

Relationships between numbers, directed numbers

Exercise 2A

1 Write down in figures the number seven thousand and fifty-nine. Is this greater or less than the number 10 410?

2 Write down the number which is
   a 1 more than 4209,
   b 1 less than 2070,
   c 10 more than 193,
   3 100 less than 5024.

3 The temperature of a room starts at −6°C. The central heating is turned on and the temperature goes up by 15°C. What is the room's new temperature?

4 Copy the following, putting the correct numbers in the boxes:

   a   ☐ 2 7
         9 4 ☐ +
      ―――――――
       1 7 ☐ 2

   b   1 ☐
        ☐ 8
        5 6 +
      ―――――――
       1 4 3

   c   4 0 7 ☐
        ☐ 8 1 −
      ―――――――
       ☐ 7 0 4

   d   7 5 9 2
        ☐ 8 3 ☐ −
      ―――――――
        ☐ ☐ 7

5 From the numbers 1860, 2003, 11 301, 1904, write down
   a the largest number,
   b the smallest number,
   c the number which is closest to 1960.

6 A man's bank account is £50 'in the red' (that is, he owes the bank £50). How much money must he pay into the bank
   a to put his account £120 in credit?
   b to make his account only £15 in the red?

7 A boy is experimenting with his calculator, using only whole numbers under 10. In each of the following cases name two numbers which produce the display shown when they are divided

a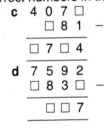

b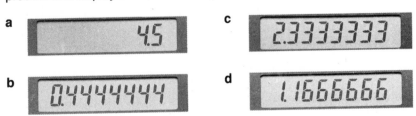

8 I play a card game in which I start with 0 points and win or lose points after each hand. How many points do I have if
  a I win 12 points, then lose 7;
  b I win 5 points, then lose 9;
  c I lose 2 points, then lose 3;
  d I win 7 points, then lose 2, then win 3;
  e I lose 8 points, then win 5, then win 7;
  f I lose 10 points, then win 8, then lose 4.

9 Write down the following numbers in figures:
  a two thousand, seven hundred and nine,
  b half a million,
  c ninety-two thousand, nine hundred and seventy-eight,
  d six hundred and four thousand and thirty-seven.

  Write down also
  e the greatest and least of these numbers

  and
  f work out the difference between them.

10 Copy the following, making each statement true by putting in either 'is less than' or 'is greater than':
  a −17 . . . 4
  b −2 . . . −9
  c 13 . . . −20
  d −50 . . . −45

11 **a** Arrange the following numbers in ascending order (that is, start with the smallest and finish with the largest):
  $$-3, 5, -11, -1, 0, 1, -8$$
  b Find the difference between the largest number and the smallest.
  c Name the number which is 10 more than the smallest number.

12 A potholer starts 150 feet below sea level.
  a What will be her final level if she climbs 60 feet?
  b How far must she climb (from her original position) to finish 70 feet above sea level?
  c If she climbs to 20 feet below sea level, then goes down twice as far as she has risen, at what level will she finish?

13 Write down the number one million, thirty-five thousand and seventeen. Is this greater or less than the number I get by adding six hundred thousand to seven hundred thousand?

14 Write down the number which is
  a 5 less than 2,
  b 7 less than −10,
  c 1 more than −3
  d 10 more than −6.

15 Thalia owes her friend 85p. She is given £1.50 pocket money, earns 25p by running an errand for her mother, spends 30p on sweets and pays off her debt to her friend. How much does she have now?

16 Work out the change in temperature in each of the following cases, saying whether it is a rise or a fall:
   a from −2°C to 7°C,
   b from −12°C to −8°C,
   c from 10°F to −20°F,
   d from −1°C to −7°C,
   e from −15°F to 19°F,
   f from −14°F to −29°F.

Exercise 2B

1 Write down in figures the number ten thousand, two hundred and one. Is this greater or less than 8479?

2 One night the temperature of a loft is recorded at 2-hourly intervals. The results are as follows:

12 p.m.	4°C
2 a.m.	−1°C
4 a.m.	−3°C
6 a.m.	−4°C
8 a.m.	2°C

   a Write down the greatest and least recorded temperatures.
   b How much does the temperature fall between 12 p.m. and 4 a.m.?
   c During which 2-hour interval is the temperature change the greatest?

3 Write down the number which is
   a 5 more than 497,
   b 10 less than 2913,
   c 100 more than 908,
   d 1000 less than 1109.

4 Copy the following, putting the correct numbers in the boxes.

   a   4 ☐ 5 9
       1 2 ☐ 8 +
       ─────────
       ☐ 0 9 ☐

   b   8 3 ☐ 4
       2 ☐ 0 7 −
       ─────────
       ☐ 8 0 ☐

   c   ☐ 7 ☐ 6
             3 ×
       ─────────
       5 ☐ 3 ☐

   d   ☐ 7 ☐
             7 ×
       ─────────
       1 9 ☐ 8

5 Business A starts with seventy thousand pounds and manages to double its money, while business B starts with a quarter of a million pounds but loses half of it. Which business is now the richer, and by how much?

6 Find the number which is
   a 6 more than −3.
   b 8 less than 1.
   c 10 less than −10.
   d 1 more than −20.

7   Write down in figures
    a the number two hundred thousand and ninety-four,
    b the number which is 10 more than this.

8   In 1986 Tariq earned £11 040, Samantha earned £9680, John earned £10 900 and Tabitha earned £200 more than John.
    a Who earned the most?
    b Whose earnings were closest to £10 000?

    In 1987 Samantha's earnings increased by £2000 and Tabitha's fell by £1000. Tariq's and John's earnings did not change.

    c Who earned the most in 1987?
    d Who earned the least in 1987?

9   If the following numbers are written in ascending order, which number will come **a** immediately after −4?   **b** immediately before −7?
                    15, −4, −18, 2, −5, −20, −7

10 A girl is trying out the $\boxed{1/x}$ button on her calculator. Which numbers give the following displays when she keys them in and presses this button?

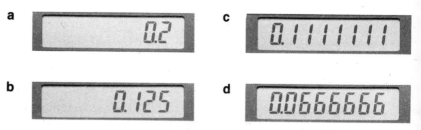

    a 0.2   **c** 0.1111111

    b 0.125   **d** 0.0666666

11 A woman's bank account is £200 in the red. She draws out a further £120, then pays in enough to put the account £20 in credit. How much does she pay in?

12 Copy the following, inserting either 'is greater than' or 'is less than':
    a 11 . . . −900
    b 9084 . . . 10 107
    c −20 . . . −21

13 Write down in figures the number three-quarters of a million. Is this greater or less than the difference between nine hundred thousand and two hundred thousand?

14 Say how far north or south of my starting point I am after each of the following journeys:
    a 7 km due north, then 15 km due south,
    b 3 miles due south, then 9 miles due south,
    c 20 miles due north, then 25 miles due south, then 50 miles due north,
    d 7 km due south, then 5 km due north, then 3 km due north, then 2 km due south.

15 After winning 5 points and losing 9, a player has −10 points. How many points did she start with?

16 Work out the change in temperature in each of the following cases, saying whether it is a rise or a fall:
   a from 20°C to 4°C,
   b from 0°F to −9°F,
   c from −15°C to 5°C,
   d from 2°C to −11°C,
   e from −20°F to −18°F,
   f from −7°F to −19°F.

Inequality symbols and brackets

Exercise 3A

1 Copy the following, inserting in each case the symbol < or >:
   a 15 . . . 25
   b 3 . . . −7
   c 2040 . . . 1928
   d −12 . . . −13

2 Work out
   a 20 − (8 + 4)
   b (7 + 4) (5 − 3)
   c (12 ÷ 4) ÷ (2 × 3)
   d $(9 − 2 − 3)^2 − (7 − 8 + 3)^2$

3 Write the following statements by using the symbols ⩽ and ⩾:
   a x is greater than or equal to 5,
   b y is not more than 8,
   c w is at least 6,
   d z is no smaller than t.

4 The statement 'x is between 5 and 10' can be written $5 < x < 10$.
   Express the following statements in a similar way:
   a y is between 0 and 20,
   b s is more than 8 but less than 15,
   c x is more than 2 but not more than 12,
   d z is positive, and less than or equal to 40,
   e w is not positive and not less than −10.

5 Copy the following, inserting brackets to make the statements true:
   a 2 × 5 − 3 = 4
   b 10 − 2 × 5 = 40
   c 24 ÷ 6 ÷ 2 = 2
   d 12 − 8 − 10 + 6 = 8
   e 8 + 3 × 4 − 5 = 15
   f 12 − 6 ÷ 3 − 1 = 3

6 Letting a man's earnings be E, write the following statements by using E and the symbols $<$, $\leqslant$, $>$ and $\geqslant$.
  a The man earns over £50.
  b His earnings are not more than £75.
  c He earns at least £300.
  d His earnings are more than £30 and less than £60.

7 In each of the following cases find a whole number N which satisfies all the given conditions:
  a $N > 20$, $N < 30$, N is divisible by 9.
  b $N \leqslant 37$, $N > 31$, N is a prime number.
  c $40 < N < 50$, N is divisible by 14.

Exercise 3B

1 Copy the following, inserting in each case the symbol $<$ or $>$:
  a $61 \ldots 57$
  b $-100 \ldots 23$
  c $0 \ldots -15$
  d $-44 \ldots -37$

2 Work out
  a $10 - (8 + 4 - 5)$
  b $(12 - 7)(4 + 3)$
  c $(24 \div 2) \div (12 \div 3)$
  d $5^2 - (5 - 2)^2$

3 Write the following statements by using the symbols $\leqslant$ and $\geqslant$:
  a p is less than or equal to 20,
  b r is at least as great as s,
  c y is not less than 150,
  d w is not more than z.

4 Copy the following, inserting brackets to make the statements true:
  a $14 - 6 \div 2 = 11$
  b $12 - 8 + 1 - 3 = 6$
  c $40 \div 8 \div 2 = 2\frac{1}{2}$
  d $7 - 5 \times 6 + 1 = 14$
  e $2 \times 1 - 3 + 2 = 0$
  f $6 \div 2 + 4 = 4 - 1 + 2$

5 Express the following statements by using only the symbols $<$ and $\leqslant$:
  a x is between 7 and 8,
  b y is negative and more than -10,
  c w is at least 4 but not more than 12,
  d z is less than 12 but not negative.

6 Letting Carmel's age be c, Peter's age be p and Sofia's age be s, write the following statements by using the inequality symbols.
  a Carmel is older than Peter.
  b Sofia is at least as old as Carmel.
  c Peter is not younger than Sofia.
  d Sofia is younger than Peter, who is younger than Carmel.

7   In each of the following cases find all the whole numbers N which satisfy all of the given conditions.
  a $20 < N < 30$, N is even.
  b $7 \leqslant N < 10$.
  c $N > -7$, $N \leqslant -3$.
  d $5 < N < 10$, $7 < N < 14$.
  e $2 < N \leqslant 18$, N is even, N is divisible by 3.

Types of numbers

Note: *Do not use a calculator in Exercises 4A and 4B.*

Exercise 4A

1   From the following numbers list **a** the odd numbers, and **b** the even numbers:
              7, 23, 16, 149, 80, 2061, 978

2   Write down the multiples of 3 between 10 and 25.

3   Write down the values of
  a 3^2 **b** 5^2 **c** 8^2

4   Say which of the following are square numbers:
              15, 4, 48, 81, 1, 10, 27, 49

5   From all the whole numbers up to and including 30, write down
  a all the multiples of 5,
  b all the multiples of 9,
  c a number which is a multiple of 8 and differs by 5 from a multiple of 7.

6   The first three prime numbers are 2, 3, 5. Write down the next five prime numbers.

7   In each of the following cases say whether or not the given number is a prime:
  a 39   **b** 23   **c** 52   **d** 41   **e** 91

8   Work out
  a 2^3 **b** 5^3 **c** 10^3

9   When the number 12 is **factorised into prime numbers** it is written as $2 \times 2 \times 3$. Factorise the following numbers into primes:
  a 15   **b** 20   **c** 42   **d** 16   **e** 99

10   Which number is a factor of all even numbers?

11   Is there any number (other than 1) which is a factor of all odd numbers?

12   In each of the following cases say whether or not the given number has a factor of 5:
  a 38   **b** 45   **c** 60   **d** 122   **e** 3015

13 In each of the following cases say whether or not the given number has a factor of 3:
a 18 **b** 34 **c** 72 **d** 196 **e** 2685

14 In each of the following cases say whether or not the given number is a prime:
a 63 **b** 51 **c** 73 **d** 121 **e** 89 **f** 177

15 Find the square roots of the following numbers:
a 4 **b** 36 **c** 121 **d** 225

16 If a square has an area of 100 square cm, what is the length of each of its sides?

17 Fine the side lengths of the squares whose areas are
a 49 square cm,
b 144 square cm,
c 196 square cm.

18 What can you say about the square root of
a any even square number?
b any odd square number?

19 Find $\sqrt{289}$, given that it is either 16, 17 or 18.

20 Find $\sqrt{576}$, given that it is either 23, 24, 25 or 26.

21 Say whether each of the following statements is true or false:
a all multiples of 4 are even.
b all prime numbers are odd.
c all multiples of odd numbers are odd.
d an odd number added to an odd number always gives an even number.
e an odd number multiplied by an odd number always gives an odd number.

Exercise 4B

1 How many odd numbers are there between
a 10 and 20?
b 15 and 31 inclusive?
c 0 and 100?

2 List all the multiples of 4 between 30 and 50.

3 List all the numbers below 25 which are both even and multiples of 3. What property do all these numbers have?

4 Work out
a 4^2 **b** 7^2 **c** 9^2 **d** 13^2

5 Say which of the following are square numbers:
64, 12, 40, 125, 9, 324, 200, 1000

6 In each of the following cases say whether or not the given number is a prime:
a 13 **b** 46 **c** 57 **d** 53 **e** 97

7 Factorise the following numbers into primes:
a 21 **b** 18 **c** 40 **d** 52 **e** 85 **f** 132

8 Factorise
   a 231, given that 11 is a factor,
   b 1105, given that 13 is a factor.

9 Work out
   a 3^3 **b** 4^3 **c** 7^3

10 List all the prime numbers between 80 and 100.

11 In each of the following cases say whether or not the given number has a factor of 7:
   a 56 **b** 76 **c** 98 **d** 143 **e** 2107

12 What is the largest number below 60 which is a multiple of both 2 and 9?

13 What is the smallest number above 50 which is a multiple of both 2 and 8?

14 Find the square roots of
   a 25 **b** 256 **c** 900

15 Find $\sqrt{1369}$, given that it is either 36, 37 or 38.

16 Between 60 and 90 there is just one pair of consecutive odd numbers, both of which are prime. What are these numbers?

17 Which square number, between 10 and 100, is also a perfect cube?

18 Say whether each of the following statements is true or false:
   a all multiples of 6 are multiples of 3.
   b all multiples of even numbers are even.
   c a prime number added to a prime number always gives a prime number.
   d an even number added to an odd number always gives an odd number.
   e all factors of even numbers are even.
   f the square of an odd number must be odd, and the square of an even number must be even.

Natural numbers, integers, rational and irrational numbers, common factors and multiples

Note: *In these exercises 0 will be considered to be a natural number.*

1 From the following numbers list **a** the natural numbers, and **b** the integers:

$$7, -4, 2\tfrac{1}{2}, -12\tfrac{1}{4}, 5, 23, -11$$

2 State **a** the number of natural numbers, and **b** the number of integers, between $-5\frac{1}{2}$ and $7\frac{1}{2}$.

3 By listing the first few multiples of 4 and of 6, find
   a the first three common multiples of 4 and 6.
   b their lowest common multiple (LCM).

4 Find the LCM of
   a 3 and 5,
   b 2 and 8,
   c 10 and 15,
   d 12 and 16.

5 In each of the following cases say whether the given number is rational or irrational:
   a $2\cdot3$ **b** π **c** $\sqrt{7}$ **d** $\sqrt{6\frac{1}{4}}$ **e** $5\frac{2}{7}$

6 Write down
   a the common prime factors of 30 and 45.
   b the highest number which divides into both 30 and 45 (this is called their **highest common factor** or HCF).

7 Find the HCF of
   a 18 and 24,
   b 12 and 20,
   c 44 and 66,
   d 48 and 80.

8 What is the HCF of any two different prime numbers?

9 Find **a** the number of natural numbers, and **b** the number of integers, in the interval of $-12 < x \leqslant 20$.

10 From the following numbers list **a** the integers, and **b** the irrational numbers:
$$-15, \sqrt{5}, 3\cdot6, \sqrt{49}, \sqrt[3]{4}, 5\cdot\dot{7}, \sqrt{-9}$$

11 Find the LCM of
   a 8, 12 and 20,
   b 5, 9 and 15,
   c 8, 9 and 12,
   d 14, 28 and 42.

12 Find the HCF of
   a 16, 24 and 32,
   b 30, 60 and 75,
   c 27, 54 and 135.

13 Say in each case whether the given statement is true or false:
   a all natural numbers are integers.
   b some integers are irrational.
   c all recurring decimals are rational.
   d the LCM of any set of different prime numbers is the product of the numbers.

Exercise 5B

1   From the following numbers list **a** the natural numbers, and **b** the integers:
$$-2, 5\tfrac{1}{3}, 29, 104, -14, 71$$

2   How many natural numbers are there
   a   below 20?
   b   between -12 and -3?

3   What is the largest negative integer?

4   State
   a   the first three common multiples of 2 and 6,
   b   the common prime factors of 42 and 70.

5   Find the LCM of
   a   3 and 15,
   b   2, 6 and 8,
   c   11 and 20,
   d   4, 6, 12 and 36,
   e   22, 33 and 44.

6   Find the HCF of
   a   15 and 25,
   b   6, 9 and 20,
   c   13 and 39,
   d   12, 18 and 42,
   e   51, 68 and 85.

7   Say in each case whether the given number is rational or irrational:
   a $-4\tfrac{2}{3}$ **c** $\sqrt{2}$ **e** $1\cdot6$
   b $3\tfrac{1}{7}$ **d** $\sqrt[3]{100}$ **f** $5\cdot049$

8   From the following numbers list **a** the natural numbers, and **b** the numbers which are rational but not natural:
$$-\sqrt{11}, 45, \sqrt{16}, 2\tfrac{1}{2}, \sqrt[3]{10}, -8$$

9   Find
   a   the number of natural numbers in the interval $12 < x \leqslant 17$,
   b   the number of integers in the interval $-10 < x < -2$,
   c   the number of non-natural integers in the interval $-3 < x < 3$.

10   Find the LCM and the HCF of each of the following sets of numbers:
   a   15, 30 and 40,
   b   4, 8, 16 and 32,
   c   36, 60 and 180,
   d   33, 55 and 66,
   e   38, 57 and 95,
   f   2, 11 and 13.

11   Say in each case whether the given statement is true or false:
   a   there are no negative natural numbers.
   b   all square roots of natural numbers are irrational.
   c   some irrational numbers are natural numbers.
   d   between any two integers there is an infinite number of rational numbers.
   e   if two numbers have no common factors other than 1, the LCM of the numbers is obtained by multiplying them together.

15

Number patterns and sequences

1 Here is a sequence of patterns made with dots.

        ●   ●●   ●●●
                   ●   ●●
                            ●

   a Draw the next two patterns in the sequence.
   b The numbers of dots in the patterns form a sequence of numbers
      called **triangular numbers**:

                   1, 3, 6 . . .

      Write down the next three triangular numbers.

2 Write down the next three numbers in each of the following
   sequences:
   a 3, 7, 11, 15;
   b 20, 23, 26, 29;
   c 21, 19, 17, 15.

3 The first few **square numbers** are
                 1, 4, 9, 16
   a Write down the next three square numbers.
   b Work out the differences between pairs of successive square
      numbers. (For example, the difference between the first and the
      second is 3.) What are these numbers called?

4 Write down the next two numbers in each of the following sequences:
   a 1, 2, 4, 8;
   b 1, 3, 9, 27;
   c 80, 40, 20.

5 A man saves £50 in 1986, £60 in 1987, and increases his savings by
   £10 each year until his **total** savings reach £350. Then he decreases
   his savings by £5 each year.
   a In which year do his total savings reach £350?
   b In which year does he save £75?
   c In which year do his total savings exceed £750?

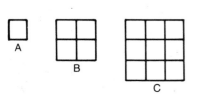

6 The series of patterns shown on the left, A, B and C, could be made
   with matches.
   a Draw the next pattern, D, in the series.
   b Count the number of squares of the size of A that occur in each
      pattern, and write down the number of squares of this size that
      would occur in patterns E and F.
   c Copy and complete the following table:

Pattern	A	B	C	D
Number of matches	4	12		
Number of extra matches		8		

d By carrying on the sequence in the last row of your table, work out the number of matches that would be needed for patterns E and F.

7 Find the missing terms in the following sequences:
a 6, 8, *, 12, 14;
b 10, 15, *, *, 30;
c 4, 9, 16, *, 36;
d 3, 6, 12, *, 48.

8 In the following sequence, each number (except the first two) is obtained by adding the two numbers just before it:
0, 1, 1, 2, 3
a Carry on the sequence until you reach a number which is more than 50.
b Another sequence of the same kind is
*, *, 6, 10, 16, 26
Work out the first two terms of this sequence.

9 A sequence formed by the rule '**double the last number and take away 1**' is
2, 3, 5, 9, 17
The following sequences are formed by similar rules. In each case find the rule and work out the next two numbers:
a 3, 7, 15, 31;
b 2, 4, 10, 28;
c 1, 2, 7, 32.

10 Two lines can cross at one point (at most), and three lines can cross at three points:

Two lines,   Three lines,
one point   three points

a If a fourth line is added to the second diagram, what is the maximum number of **extra** crossing points that it can make?
b From your answer to **a**, how many crossing points altogether can be made with four lines?
c By filling in the last row first, complete the following table:

Number of lines	2	3	4	5	6
Maximum number of crossing points	1	3			
Maximum number of extra crossing points		2			

d What are the numbers in the second row called?

11 By finding a pattern in the **differences** between successive numbers, work out the next two numbers in each of the following sequences:
a 2, 3, 5, 8, 12;
b 1, 2, 5, 10, 17;
c 4, 10, 15, 19, 22;
d 0, 1, 5, 12, 22.

12 In the following sequence of equations, work out the values of a, b, x and y:

$$2(3 - 1) = 4$$
$$3(5 - 1) = 12$$
$$4(7 - 1) = 24$$
$$\vdots$$
$$6(a - 1) = b$$
$$\vdots$$
$$x(15 - 1) = y$$

Exercise 6B

1 Write down the next three numbers in each of the following sequences:
 a 9, 13, 17, 21;
 b 15, 12, 9, 6;
 c 1, 8, 15, 22.

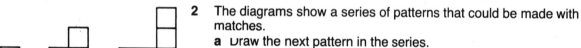

2 The diagrams show a series of patterns that could be made with matches.
 a Draw the next pattern in the series.
 b Count the number of squares in each of the patterns, and write down the number of squares in the fourth, fifth and sixth patterns of the series.
 c Count the number of matches in each of the patterns, and write down the number of matches in the fourth, fifth and sixth patterns of the series.

3 A car which is slowing down travels 20 metres in the 1st second, $18\frac{1}{2}$ metres in the 2nd second, 17 metres in the 3rd second, and so on. If it continues to slow down at the same rate, how far will it travel
 a in the 7th second?
 b altogether in the first 5 seconds?

4 Write down the next two numbers in each of the following sequences:
 a 3, 6, 12, 24;
 b 1, 4, 16, 64;
 c 400, 200, 100, 50.

5 In the following triangle (which is called **Pascal's triangle**), the numbers at the ends of the rows are all ones, and each other number is obtained from the two numbers just above it:

```
        1
      1   1
    1   2   1
  1   3   3   1
```

Copy the triangle and add the next three rows.

6 Find the missing terms in the following sequences:
 a 13, 15, *, 19, 21;
 b 25, *, 49, 64;
 c 30, 27, *, *, 18;
 d $\frac{1}{2}$, 1, 2, *, 8.

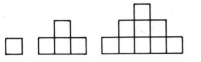

7 The diagrams represent a series of towers made with bricks.
  a Draw the next tower in the series.
  b Count the number of bricks in each tower. What are these numbers called?
  c Without drawing the tower, find the number of bricks that would be needed for the sixth tower in the series.

8 In the following sequences each number (except the first two) is obtained from the two numbers just before it. Find the next two numbers in each sequence.
  a 1, 3, 4, 7, 11;
  b 1, 2, 2, 4, 8;
  c 16, 10, 6, 4, 2.

9 **a** Find the next number in the following sequence, given that the rule is '**square the last number and add 2**':
$$1, 3, 11$$
  b Find the first four numbers in the sequence which starts with 3 and is formed by the rule '**square the last number and take away 5**'.

10 Some football teams play in a league in which the rule is '**all play all twice**'. If there were just 3 teams (A, B and C) in the league, the following table would show all the games that had to be played.

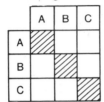

  a By drawing tables like the one shown, and choosing your own teams, work out the total number of games that would have to be played in leagues with 2 teams, with 3 teams, with 4 teams and with 5 teams.
  b The numbers you have obtained in **a** should form a pattern. By working out the differences between pairs of successive numbers in this pattern, find the number of games that would have to be played in leagues with 6 teams and with 7 teams.
  c What is the relationship between the numbers in your pattern and triangular numbers?

11 By finding a pattern in the differences between successive numbers, work out the next two terms in each of the following sequences:
  a 4, 5, 7, 10, 14;
  b 0, 4, 10, 18, 28;
  c 30, 29, 27, 24, 20;
  d 0, 3, 9, 18, 30.

12 In the following sequence of equations, work out the values of m, p and t:
$$(1 \times 2) - 2 = 0$$
$$(2 \times 3) - 4 = 2$$
$$(3 \times 4) - 6 = 6$$
$$\vdots$$
$$(m \times 8) - p = t$$

Fractions and Decimals

Note: *Do not use a calculator except in question 11.*

1 Reduce the following fractions to their lowest terms by dividing the numerator (top number) and denominator (bottom number) by the same number:

   a $\frac{3}{6}$ **c** $\frac{10}{15}$ **e** $\frac{14}{16}$ **g** $\frac{100}{250}$

   b $\frac{6}{8}$ **d** $\frac{4}{12}$ **f** $\frac{24}{30}$ **h** $\frac{25}{175}$

2 Express the following fractions as decimals:

   a $\frac{1}{2}$ **d** $\frac{1}{5}$ **g** $\frac{4}{5}$ **j** $\frac{7}{20}$

   b $\frac{3}{4}$ **e** $\frac{1}{100}$ **h** $\frac{1}{8}$

   c $\frac{3}{10}$ **f** $\frac{17}{100}$ **i** $\frac{5}{8}$

3 Reduce the following fractions to their lowest terms, then express them as decimals:

   a $\frac{12}{48}$ **b** $\frac{18}{30}$ **c** $\frac{15}{40}$ **d** $\frac{6}{200}$

4 Express the following decimals as fractions in their lowest terms:

   a 0·1   **c** 0·4   **e** 0·001   **g** 0·875

   b 0·25   **d** 0·09   **f** 0·15

5 Work out the following, giving the answers as fractions in their lowest terms:

   a $\frac{1}{2} + \frac{1}{4}$ **e** $\frac{2}{5} + \frac{1}{4}$ **i** $2\frac{2}{3} + 1\frac{1}{3}$

   b $\frac{1}{10} + \frac{3}{10}$ **f** $2\frac{1}{4} + 3\frac{1}{2}$ **j** $\frac{3}{5} + \frac{7}{10} + \frac{1}{2}$

   c $1\frac{1}{2} + \frac{3}{4}$ **g** $\frac{5}{8} + \frac{1}{4}$ **k** $5\frac{1}{2} + 2\frac{7}{8} + 4\frac{3}{4}$

   d $\frac{1}{6} + \frac{1}{3}$ **h** $\frac{3}{8} + \frac{1}{6} + \frac{3}{4}$

6 Work out

   a 0·7 + 0·8   **d** 0·73 − 0·26   **g** 2·95 + 1·08

   b 12 − 0·3   **e** 8 − 2·41   **h** 0·72 − 0·063

   c 0·06 + 0.49   **f** 9·4 − 3·7   **i** 15·3 − 4·94

7 Work out

   a $\frac{1}{2}$ of $\frac{2}{3}$ **d** $\frac{4}{5}$ of 20   **g** $\frac{4}{5}$ of $3\frac{1}{3}$

   b $\frac{3}{4}$ of 24   **e** $\frac{2}{3}$ of 33

   c $\frac{1}{3}$ of $\frac{6}{7}$ **f** $\frac{1}{4}$ of $1\frac{3}{5}$

8 Work out the following, giving the answers as fractions in their lowest terms:

   a $3 - \frac{1}{4}$ **d** $\frac{4}{5} - \frac{1}{3}$ **g** $7 - 2\frac{1}{3}$

   b $\frac{1}{3} - \frac{1}{6}$ **e** $\frac{8}{9} - \frac{5}{6}$ **h** $6\frac{3}{4} - 4\frac{5}{8}$

   c $\frac{7}{8} - \frac{1}{4}$ **f** $5 - 1\frac{3}{4}$ **i** $5\frac{2}{3} - 1\frac{1}{9}$

9 Work out

a $0{\cdot}2 \times 7$ d $0{\cdot}1 \times 0{\cdot}4$ g $0{\cdot}2 \times 0{\cdot}3 \times 0{\cdot}7$

b $5 \times 0{\cdot}4$ e $2{\cdot}3 \times 0{\cdot}6$ h $12 \times 0{\cdot}4 \times 0{\cdot}03$

c $6 \times 0{\cdot}03$ f $4{\cdot}21 \times 0{\cdot}02$

10 Work out

a $2 \div 0{\cdot}2$ c $4 \div 0{\cdot}25$ e $0{\cdot}14 \div 0{\cdot}7$

b $6 \div 0{\cdot}5$ d $0{\cdot}4 \div 0{\cdot}02$ f $0{\cdot}036 \div 0{\cdot}03$

11 Use your calculator to convert the following fractions to decimals, giving the answer to two decimal places:

a $\frac{1}{7}$ b $\frac{8}{9}$ c $\frac{2}{11}$ d $\frac{5}{6}$ e $\frac{4}{17}$

12 By expressing all the following as fractions with the same denominator, find **a** the greatest, and **b** the least of the fractions:

$\frac{3}{4}, \frac{7}{12}, \frac{5}{6}, \frac{2}{3}, \frac{7}{8}$

13 By converting the following fractions to decimals, find **a** the greatest, and **b** the least of the fractions:

$\frac{1}{3}, \frac{2}{7}, \frac{1}{4}, \frac{3}{11}, \frac{4}{15}$

Exercise 8A

Note: *Express all fractions in their lowest terms.*

1 The circle on the left is divided into equal sectors.

a What fraction of the circle is shaded?

b To shade 0·5 of the circle how many sectors would have to be shaded?

c To shade $\frac{2}{3}$ of the circle how many sectors would have to be shaded?

2 A class takes a test with 40 questions in it. Judy gets $\frac{3}{5}$ of the questions right and Leroy gets 0·75 of them right.

a How many questions does Judy get right?

b How many questions does Leroy get right?

3 Petrol costs 38·6p per litre. How much does it cost a motorist to buy

a 10 litres?

b 4 litres?

c 27 litres?

4 In each of the following cases say what fraction of the figure is shaded:

  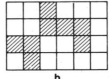

a   b   c   d

5 A man spends 0·1 of his shopping money on vegetables, 0·2 of it on fruit and 0·45 of it on meat. He spends £5 altogether.

a How much does he spend on vegetables?

b How much does he spend on fruit?

c How much does he spend on meat?

d What fraction of his money is left?

6 The following are the ingredients in a simple recipe for flapjacks:
5 oz sugar, 7 oz margarine, 8 oz oats
What fraction of the flapjacks will be
a sugar?
b oats?
c oats and margarine?

7 A girl gives half of her pocket money away and spends $\frac{3}{8}$ of it on a puzzle book.
a What fraction of her money has she used so far?
b What fraction is left?
c How much money will be left if the cost of the puzzle book was £1.20?

8 **a** Darren drinks $\frac{1}{4}$ of a bottle of milk each day. How long will 9 bottles last him?
b Darren's father smokes 1·4 packets of cigarettes each day. How long will 28 packets last him?

9 Tracy has 20p in her pocket and gives 8p of it to a collection for charity, Jane has 16p and gives 6p, while Yasmin has 25p and gives 11p.
a Express $\frac{8}{20}$, $\frac{6}{16}$ and $\frac{11}{25}$ as decimals.
b Which of the girls gives the greatest fraction of her money to the charity?

10 If there are 1·48 dollars to the pound, how many dollars will be obtained for
a £3? **b** £10? **c** £53?

11 A rectangle is 12·3 cm long and 7·2 cm wide. Work out
a its perimeter, **b** its area.

12 The following is a record of the goals scored by Arsenal football team in a series of matches:

Goals scored	0	1	2	3
Number of matches	3	6	5	1

In what fraction of the matches played did the team score:
a 2 goals?
b 1 goal?
c fewer than 2 goals?

13 A traveller needs to obtain 100 Swiss francs from his bank. If the exchange rate is 2·5 francs to the pound, how much will he have to pay in pounds?

14 A girl cycles, on average, 0·4 miles each minute.
a What is her average speed in miles per hour?
b How long will she take to travel 20 miles?
c How long will she take to travel 36 miles?

15 Mr Handa has a win of £750 on the football pools. He gives $\frac{2}{5}$ of it to his wife and $\frac{1}{6}$ of the remainder to his son Dilip.
a How much does Mrs Handa get?
b How much does Dilip get?
c What fraction of the win does Mr Handa keep for himself?

16 An overweight man sets out to lose $\frac{3}{4}$ of a pound each day and his wife sets out to lose $\frac{2}{3}$ of a pound.

    a How much weight do each of them hope to lose in a week?

    b In how many days does the man hope to lose 18 pounds and how much does his wife hope to lose in the same time?

Exercise 8B

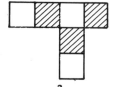

a

b

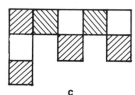

c

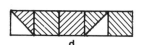

d

1 Say what fraction of each of the figures **a** to **d** on the left is shaded.

2 Wayne has to make a journey of 80 miles. He travels 0·75 of the way by train and 0·8 of the rest by bus.

    a How far does he travel by train?

    b How far does he travel by bus?

3 **a** At a wedding reception it is estimated that each of the guests that like wine will drink, on average, $\frac{1}{4}$ of a bottle. On this basis, how many bottles will provide enough wine for 36 wine drinkers?

    b At the same reception there will be 30 beer drinkers, each of whom will probably drink, on average, 1·6 pints of beer. How many pint bottles of beer will be needed?

4 Thirty people are asked to name their favourite newspaper from the *Times*, the *Guardian*, the *Daily Mail* and the *Sun*. The results are shown in the following table:

Newspaper	*Times*	*Guardian*	*Daily Mail*	*Sun*
Number of readers	4	3	8	15

    a What fraction chose the *Sun*?

    b What fraction chose the *Guardian*?

    c What fraction chose the *Times* or the *Daily Mail*?

    d What fraction did **not** choose the *Times*?

5 A man walks, on average, 0·8 miles each day.
a How far does he walk in 30 days?
b In how many days does he walk 44 miles?

6 Carmen takes £1 to the corner shop and spends 20p on sweets and 30p on chocolate. She also buys a comic for 10p.
a What fraction of the £1 does Carmen have left?
b What fraction of the £1 does she spend on sweets?
c What fraction of the money spent on **food** goes on chocolate?

7 At a particular time 3·3 German marks can be obtained for £1.
a How many marks will be obtained for £50?
b To obtain 990 marks, how many pounds will be needed?
c How much does it cost, to the nearest penny, to buy 50 marks?

8 One week Megan spends $\frac{1}{5}$ of her pocket money on magazines, $\frac{1}{4}$ of it on an outing and $\frac{3}{10}$ on a present.
a What fraction of her pocket money has Megan spent altogether, and what fraction is left?
b If she gets £6 pocket money, how much does Megan spend on the outing and how much on the present?

9 Work out the perimeters of figures **a** and **b** on the left.

10 Mr Cohen has 50 records, 17 of which are classical, Mrs Osman has 20 records, 7 of which are classical, and Mrs Evans has 75 records, 24 of which are classical.
a Express $\frac{17}{50}$, $\frac{7}{20}$ and $\frac{24}{75}$ as decimals.
b Which of the three people has the smallest proportion of classical records?

11 What fraction of the first 20 whole numbers are **a** even numbers?
b square numbers? **c** prime numbers? (**Note:** 1 is not considered to be a prime number.)

12 a Leeds United football team score, on average, 1·8 goals per game. In how many games can the team expect to score 45 goals?
b Another team, Sunderland, score, on average, $1\frac{1}{3}$ goals per game. In how many games can the team expect to score 40 goals?

13 A man has 520 books, 130 of which are on sport. Two-thirds of the rest are novels, and 0·4 of the sporting books are on cricket.
a What fraction of the books are on sport?
b How many of the books are on cricket?
c How many of the books are novels?
d What fraction of all the books are sporting books which are not on cricket?

a
4.7
2.3

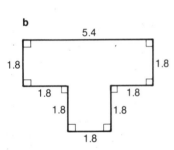

b
5.4
1.8   1.8
1.8   1.8
1.8   1.8
1.8

(The distances are in metres)

Percentage

Quick revision exercise 9

1 Express the following percentages as fractions in their lowest terms:
   a 50%   e 6%   i 28%   m $12\frac{1}{2}$%
   b 10%   f $33\frac{1}{3}$%   j 40%   n $7\frac{1}{2}$%
   c 43%   g 75%   k 65%   o $37\frac{1}{2}$%
   d 25%   h 5%   l 84%

2 Work out
   a 10% of 60   d 20% of 350   g 60% of 25
   b 25% of 80   e $33\frac{1}{3}$% of 36   h 90% of 400
   c 75% of 24   f 5% of 120

3 Express the following fractions as percentages:
   a $\frac{37}{100}$ e $\frac{2}{3}$ i $\frac{17}{20}$
   b $\frac{1}{5}$ f $\frac{11}{50}$ j $\frac{5}{8}$
   c $\frac{7}{10}$ g $\frac{7}{200}$ k $\frac{1}{12}$
   d $\frac{4}{5}$ h $\frac{9}{25}$

4 Work out
   a 3% of £2   d 7% of £9   g 17% of £8
   b 20% of £320   e 75% of £1.60   h $6\frac{1}{2}$% of £20
   c 10% of £576   f 15% of £49

Exercise 10A

1 The notice on the left is displayed by an electrical store:
   Before the sale, a radio is priced at £34 and some blank cassettes are priced at 85p each.
   a By how much will the radio's price be reduced in the sale?
   b What will be its new price?
   c How much will be saved by buying six cassettes in the sale?

2 It is calculated that, on average, 12% of a tennis player's services are faults and $2\frac{1}{2}$% are aces.
   a In 75 of the player's services, how many faults are likely to occur?
   b In 320 services, how many aces are likely to occur?

3 Mrs Baker buys a house for £52,000. When she sells it a few years later, she makes a profit of 35% on the purchase price.
   a What profit does Mrs Baker make?
   b What price does she get for the house?

4 A boy draws £6.80 out of his building society account. He spends 5% of the money on a magazine and 75% of it on a new LP.
   a How much does the magazine cost?
   b How much does the LP cost?
   c What percentage of the money drawn is left?

5 An estimate for a plumbing job is set out as follows:

Quickfix Plumbers

To:

Mr W. Walker
15 Lisbon Road
Tadcaster

Estimate

Repair of hot water tank

Parts	£17.25	....
Labour	£32.35	....
Total		....
Add VAT at 15%		....
Amount payable		....

Work out the three amounts which should go in the right-hand column.

6 One evening Bev has two hours of spare time, and spends half an hour of it talking to her friend on the telephone.
 a What percentage of her spare time does she spend on the telephone?

She then spends 60% of the remaining time watching a video.
 b How many minutes does she spend watching the video?

7 Mr Oldfield has a part-time job which pays him £48 per week. His union negotiates for a 12% rise but he is eventually given a rise of $8\frac{1}{2}\%$.
 a What rise did the union seek?
 b What rise does Mr Oldfield receive?
 c What is his final weekly wage?

8 A new car costs £5600. In its first year of use, it loses 25% of its original value.
 a By how much does the car depreciate?
 b What is its value at the end of its first year of use?

In its second year of use, the car loses only 20% of its value at the beginning of the year.

   c What is the car's value when it is two years old?

   d What percentage of its original value does the car lose in its first two years?

9 When Addie visits her uncle, who lives 60 miles away, she travels 30 miles by train and 12 miles by bus. Her uncle then meets her and takes her the rest of the way by car. What percentage of her journey does Addie make

   a by train?

   b by bus?

   c by car?

   Of the part of the journey covered by road, work out

   d the percentage which is covered by car.

10 Given that VAT is charged at 15%, work out the VAT payable on the following:

   a a roofing repair which costs £420 before VAT is added,

   b driving lessons which cost £75.40 before VAT is added,

   c an estate agent's bill of '£1935 + VAT'.

11 A double-glazing company gives an estimate of £800 for fitting some replacement windows. It has to add VAT at 15%, but it offers a discount of 5% for paying cash. Work out how much is saved by paying cash

   a if the discount is calculated before VAT is added,

   b if the discount is calculated after VAT is added.

12 A woman's salary is £920 per month. Her national insurance and superannuation cost her £164 altogether, and she is charged income tax on the rest at 29%. Work out

   a the amount of her monthly salary on which she pays income tax;

   b the amount of tax she pays per month;

   c her net monthly salary.

Exercise 10B

1 On average, Everton football team score no goals in 15% of their matches and more than three goals in 8% of their matches.

   a In 80 matches, how many times are the team likely to score no goals?

   b In 75 matches, how many times are the team likely to score more than three goals?

2 A new car is bought for £6200. When it is sold three years later it has depreciated by 45% of its purchase price.

   a By how much does the car depreciate?

   b What is the car's value when it is three years old?

Dazzle & Co.
SPECIAL SUMMER
OFFER!

25%
DISCOUNT on
purchases totalling
up to £50!!

30%
DISCOUNT on
purchases totalling
£50 or over!!

3 In a $2\frac{1}{2}$ hour examination, Jamila spends half an hour on the first question. She then devotes 5% of her remaining time to reading the other questions.
   a What percentage of her total time does Jamila spend on the first question?
   b How long does she spend reading the other questions?

4 A clothes shop displays the notice on the left in its window:
A man buys three T-shirts priced at £9.50 each and a pair of shorts priced at £6.30.
   a What is the total price of these articles before the price is reduced?
   b How much is the discount on the articles?
   c What is their final price?

A woman buys a cotton dress priced at £29.90 and two swimsuits at £17.30 each.
   d Work out the price she actually pays for these articles.

5 A woman takes out a mortgage of £18 000 with a building society which charges interest of 11% per annum.
   a How much interest does the woman have to pay in the first year?
   b If she pays the interest in 12 equal monthly instalments, how much is each instalment?

6 A school has 1000 pupils in 1975 and 880 in 1980.
   a What is the fall in the school's roll between 1975 and 1980?
   b What is the fall in roll as a percentage of the roll in 1975?

Between 1980 and 1985, the roll increases by $2\frac{1}{2}$% of the 1980 roll.
   c By how much does the roll increase?
   d What is the roll in 1985?

7 In a mock general election at a school, 450 pupils vote Conservative, 320 vote Labour and 280 vote Alliance. A month later the election is repeated, when 18% of the original Conservative supporters vote Alliance and 5% of the original Labour supporters vote Alliance. All the other pupils vote as they did at the previous election.

In the second election, how many pupils vote
   a Conservative?   **b** Labour?   **c** Alliance?

8 A sports club charges £14 per hour plus VAT at 15% to use its squash court. Work out the total cost of
   a 5 games of 1 hour each.
   b 6 hours per week for 10 weeks.

9 In a survey of 350 college students, 34% of the students name football as their favourite sport and 26% give cricket as their favourite.
   a How many students choose football?
   b How many students choose cricket?
   c What percentage of all the students asked give neither football nor cricket?

10 A microwave oven costs £174 for cash. It can also be paid for over a year in six equal instalments, but it then costs 16% more altogether.
   a How much extra does the microwave oven cost if paid for in instalments?
   b How much does it cost altogether in this case?
   c How much is each instalment?

11 Mr Andrews buys a house in 1978 for £20 000. In 1982 he sells it to Mr Shah for £28 000, and in 1985 Mr Shah himself sells it, making a profit of 25% on his own purchase price.
  a Express the profit Mr Andrews makes as a percentage of his purchase price.
  b Find the price Mr Shah receives for the house.
  c Find the total increase in the house's value between 1978 and 1985.
  d Express the total increase as a percentage of the house's value in 1978.

12 A man earns a salary of £14 000 per year. His employer deducts 12% of this for national insurance and superannuation, and he pays tax on the rest at 29%. Work out
  a how much of the man's income is deducted by his employer;
  b how much remains after the deduction;
  c how much tax he pays;
  d his net annual income.

Further percentage

Quick revision exercise 11

1 Express the following decimals as percentages:
  a 0·3 **b** 0·52 **c** 0·08 **d** 0·137

2 Use your calculator to convert the following fractions to percentages, giving the answers to the nearest whole number:
  a $\frac{5}{7}$ **b** $\frac{2}{13}$ **c** $\frac{7}{9}$ **d** $\frac{4}{17}$

3 Work out
  a 10% more than 130
  b 7% less than 500
  c 25% more than 28
  d 15% less than 80
  e 4% more than 725
  f 82% less than 1400
  g $37\frac{1}{2}$% more than 40
  h $33\frac{1}{3}$% less than 171

4 Express
  a 9 as a percentage of 45
  b 38 as a percentage of 380
  c 12 as a percentage of 300
  d 18 as a percentage of 120
  e 23 as a percentage of 92
  f 2000 as a percentage of 2500
  g 3·5 as a percentage of 10·5
  h 126 as a percentage of 360
  i 1·54 as a percentage of 1·75

5 Find the percentage gain or loss on an article which is bought and sold, given that
   a cost price = £8, selling price = £10
   b cost price = £200, selling price = £220
   c cost price = £60, selling price = £36
   d cost price = £4, selling price = £3.72
   e cost price = £7500, selling price = £6375
   f cost price = £1.20, selling price = £1.62
   g cost price = £4.75, selling price = £5.89

6 Work out the sum of money which is obtained when
   a £2 is increased by 5%   **d** £12.75 is decreased by 8%
   b £3.50 is increased by 20%   **e** £3700 is increased by 19%
   c £26 is decreased by 75%   **f** £19.40 is decreased by 45%

7 Express
   a 67p as a percentage of £1.34   **d** £3.60 as a percentage of £24
   b £1.10 as a percentage of £22   **e** £3.90 as a percentage of £7.50
   c 5p as a percentage of £2   **f** £11.84 as a percentage of £18.50

8 An article is bought and then sold. Find its cost price, given that
   a selling price = £60, profit = 25%
   b selling price = £2.80, profit = 12%
   c selling price = £448, loss = 20%
   d selling price = £3660, loss = 70%
   e selling price = 92p, profit = 15%
   f selling price = £3.78, loss = 28%
   (**Note:** percentage profit or loss is always calculated using the cost price.)

Exercise 12A

1 A cricket ground which can seat 24 000 spectators has a crowd of 16 750 on the first day of a test match.
   a Find, to the nearest whole number, the percentage of seats which are filled.

   On the second day of the match, the attendance increases by 8%.
   b Find the number of spectators on the second day.

2 A car is bought for £8500 and sold for £6460.
   a Find the car's percentage loss of value.

   The car's next owner makes some improvements to it and manages to sell it at a profit of 5%.
   b Find the price obtained by the second owner.

3 Two married couples stay for one night at a seaside town. They book bed and breakfast at an hotel, which costs £24 per person plus VAT at 15%, and they also have dinner at a restaurant, for which they pay £32.40 for the four of them plus a service charge of 10%. Work out

a the hotel bill,
b the bill for the dinner,
c the total cost of the stay at the town.

4 The number 216 is mistakenly written 261. Find the percentage error, to the nearest whole number.

5 An A-level mathematics group consists of 28 students, each of whom has to choose between mechanics and statistics. At the beginning of the course there are 20 mechanics students, but 4 of these switch to statistics during the first term. None of the statistics students switch to mechanics. Work out, to the nearest whole number where appropriate:
a the percentage of the class that originally chooses mechanics,
b the percentage of the class that studies mechanics at the end of the first term.
c the percentage drop in the number of mechanics students during the first term.
d the percentage increase in the number of statistics students during the first term.

6 A shopkeeper buys eggs in batches of 120 for £8 per batch. On average, 5% of the eggs get broken and the rest are sold in boxes of six.
a How many boxes of six eggs are obtained from a batch of 120?

The shopkeeper aims to make a profit of at least 12% on her outlay.
b What is 12% more than £8?
c How much should the shopkeeper charge for each box of six eggs?

7 In 1986 the charges for a snooker club outing are as follows:

    hire of coach   £32
    meals, entrance charges, etc.   £8.50 per head

In 1987 the coach charge rises to £36 and it is estimated that the other charges will rise by 8%. Work out
a the percentage rise in the coach charge,
b the expected cost per head of the other items.

It is planned to take a party of 30 people on the 1987 outing. Work out, on the basis of the above estimate,
c the total cost of the outing,
d the amount each person will have to pay if the total cost is divided equally among all the members of the party.

If, in fact, each person is charged £11, work out
e the profit made by the snooker club,
f the profit as a percentage of the total cost, to the nearest whole number.

8 A building society offers two savings accounts in the advertisement on the left.
Mr McGregor requires immediate access to his money. He invests £400 in the Deposit Account on 1 January and withdraws £120 of it six months later. On the following 31 December, work out
a how much interest he receives on the £120 he withdrew,
b how much interest he receives on the rest of his investment,
c how much he has in his account after the interest is added.

BUILDING SOCIETY

GOLD STAR ACCOUNT — 9.25% per annum
(3 months notice of withdrawals required)

DEPOSIT ACCOUNT — 8.5% per annum
(no notice of withdrawals required)

Interest is added to your account on
31 December each year

Mrs Mtebe wants the highest possible interest. She invested £640 on 31 March in the Gold Star Account. On the following 31 December, work out

    d how much interest is added to her account,

    e how much extra interest she obtains by using the Gold Star Account rather than the Deposit Account.

9 An electrical shop offers a discount of 5% for cash.

    a A personal stereo is priced in the window at £27.40. What does it cost for cash?

    b A dishwasher is obtained by paying £418 cash. What was its price before the discount?

    c A hair dryer is bought for cash at a discount of 40p. How much is paid for it?

10 Mr O'Rourke, Mr Evans and Ms McAllister work for the same computer firm and know that they will receive the same percentage wage rise.

    a Mr O'Rourke is told that his wages will rise from £82.40 to £88.17. Work out the percentage rise, to the nearest whole number.

    b Mr Evans earns £78.60 before the increase. What will be his new wage, to the nearest penny?

    c Ms McAllister calculates that after the rise she will get £88.81. What is her wage before the rise?

Exercise 12B

Note: *Give percentages which do not come out exactly to the nearest whole number.*

1 In a test with 65 questions in it, Fatima gets 40 questions right and Paul gets 15% fewer questions right than Fatima.

    a What percentage of the questions does Fatima get right?

    b How many questions does Paul get right?

2 Gary earns £7.50 per week at a part-time job, and spends 60% of the money on clothes.

    a How much does he spend per week on clothes?

After a year at the job he is given a 10% wage rise, but does not alter the amount he spends on clothes.

    b What is Gary's new weekly wage?

    c What percentage of his wage does he now spend on clothes?

3 A rectangular room which really measures 19 feet by 15 feet is incorrectly decribed by an estate agent as measuring 20 feet by 16 feet. Work out the percentage error in

    a the perimeter of the room.

    b the area of the room.

4 A shopkeeper buys 40 ball-point pens for 10p each and 60 pencils for 8p each. She sells the pens for 14p each and the pencils for 10p each. Work out
   a the percentage profit she makes on the pens,
   b the percentage profit she makes on the pencils,
   c the total price she pays for the pens and pencils,
   d the total price she receives when they are all sold,
   e the overall percentage profit she makes.

5 A woman owns 160 books, of which 24 are on golf, 16 are on tennis and the rest are on non-sporting subjects. Work out the percentage of the books which are on
   a sport,
   b golf.

   She later buys some more books, increasing the total number by 20%. Given that she buys 14 non-sporting books and increases the number of books on tennis by $37\frac{1}{2}$%, work out
   c the percentage increase in the number of books on golf,
   d the percentage increase in the number of books on sport.

6 A sales person receives a fixed payment of £450 per month and a commission of 20% on the goods he sells. One month he makes a total of £700.
   a Work out the value of the goods he sells.

   In the following month his sales drop by 8%. Work out
   b the commission he receives that month,
   c the percentage decrease in his total salary.

7 A quarterly telephone bill is presented as follows:

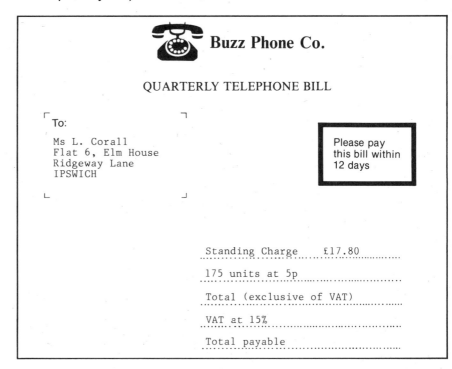

Buzz Phone Co.

QUARTERLY TELEPHONE BILL

To:

Ms L. Corall
Flat 6, Elm House
Ridgeway Lane
IPSWICH

Please pay
this bill within
12 days

Standing Charge   £17.80

175 units at 5p

Total (exclusive of VAT)

VAT at 15%

Total payable

Work out
a the four amounts which should go in the right-hand column,
b the cost of the units used as a percentage of the total cost.

In the following quarter the owner of the telephone increases the number of units she uses by 12%. The standing charge and the cost of each unit are unchanged. Work out
c the number of units now used,
d the new total payable,
e the percentage increase in the total payable.

8 A woman's salary is £14 200 in 1988. In 1989 she receives a 5% increase and in 1990 her increase is £1050. Work out
a her salary in 1989,
b the percentage increase she gets in 1990.

9 A car depreciates by 30% in its first year of use and by 26% in its second. Given that it is worth £8400 when one year old, work out
a its value when two years old,
b its value when new.

10 An estate agent's charge for selling a house is 2% of the price obtained for the house plus VAT at 15%. The agent's final bill to a client is £1104. Work out
a the agent's charge before the addition of VAT,
b the price of the house that was sold.

Units, Measurement, Estimation

Quick revision exercise 13

1 Convert to grams:
   a 2 kg   **b** 1400 mg   **c** 0·85 kg   **d** 12·7 kg   **e** 54 400 mg

2 Convert to centimetres:
   a 5 m   **b** 37 mm   **c** 0·64 m   **d** 0·5 km   **e** 835 mm

3 Convert to kilograms:
   a 8500 g   **b** 400 g   **c** 2 t   **d** 38·4 t   **e** 15 200 g

4 Convert to centilitres:
   a 7 litres   **b** 430 ml   **c** 0·62 litres   **d** 23 ml

5 Convert to metres:
   a 436 cm   **b** 7 km   **c** 2400 mm   **d** 39 cm   **e** 0·82 km

6 Convert to tonnes:
   a 8000 kg   **b** 730 kg   **c** 67 000 g   **d** 57 620 kg

7 Convert to millilitres:
   a 1·5 litres   **b** 6 cl   **c** 0·45 litres   **d** 0·47 cl

8 Express to the nearest centimetre:
   a 2·4 cm   **b** 37·9 cm   **c** 56 mm   **d** 123 mm

9 Express to the nearest kilogram:
   a 48·7 kg   **b** 0·85 kg   **c** 3426 g   **d** 3·52 kg   **e** 58 103 g

10 Express to the nearest metre:
   a 13·7 m   **b** 438·49 m   **c** 209 cm   **d** 3280 cm   **e** 74 478 mm

11 Express to the nearest 10:
   a 74   **b** 678   **c** 96   **d** 25·7   **e** 7 × 19·4

12 Express to the nearest 100:
   a 680   **b** 5463   **c** 1642·6   **d** 32 560   **e** 20 × 478

Exercise 14A

1 Say which of the units **kilometres**, **metres**, **centimetres or millimetres** it would be best to use to measure each of the following:
   a the height of a room,
   b the distance from Birmingham to Liverpool,
   c the length of your foot,
   d the thickness of a piece of paper,
   e the length of a football pitch.

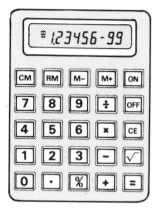

2 The weights of a set of objects are found to be 1·5 g, 0·8 kg, 70 g, 6 kg and 20 mg. The objects (listed in a different order) are
a a typewriter, **b** a needle, **c** a tube of toothpaste, **d** a stick of chalk and **e** a dictionary.
State the weight of each of the objects.

3 The calculator shown is 7·53 cm wide. Estimate its length, to the nearest centimetre.

4 A shopper orders three $2\frac{1}{2}$ kg bags of potatoes, $1\frac{1}{4}$ kg of carrots, 1100 g of oranges and 300 g of tomatoes. Work out the total weight of his order
a in kilograms,
b in grams.

Later he also orders some mushrooms, raising the total weight to 10·4 kg.
c How many grams of mushrooms does he order?

5 Ashok is 140 cm tall and Bindi is $1\frac{3}{5}$ m tall. Work out
a Ashok's height in metres,
b Bindi's height in centimetres,
c the difference between their heights, in centimetres.

6

Three glasses of lemonade are poured out from a $1\frac{1}{2}$ litre bottle. The glasses contain 35 cl, 0·25 litres and 200 ml.
a How much lemonade is poured out altogether, in centilitres?
b How much remains in the bottle, in millilitres?

7 A shopkeeper is supplied with pencils in boxes of 40. The pencils have an average mass of 800 mg and the boxes have a mass of 12 g each. Work out
a the total mass, in grams, of one box of pencils,
b the number of boxes of pencils that would have a mass of just over 1 kg.

8

A piece of measuring tape 6 m long is cut into two pieces by a pair of scissors placed as shown. Estimate the length of the longer piece, to the nearest centimetre.

9 Kelvin needs half a pound of sultanas for a recipe. In his local grocers the sultanas are sold in packets of 150 g, 200 g, 250 g and 300 g. He knows that there are about 28 grams to the ounce. Which packet should he buy to have just enough for the recipe with as little as possible left over?

10 To find out roughly how thick an ordinary piece of paper is, a girl measures the thickness of 100 pages of one of her books. This turns out to be about $\frac{1}{2}$ cm.
   a Estimate the thickness of one page, in millimetres.
   b Work out the approximate thickness of 40 pages, in millimetres.

11 A small spoon which holds 3 ml is supplied to be used with a bottle of medicine which contains 20 cl of medicine. Work out
   a how many complete doses of one spoonful the bottle will supply,
   b how much medicine will be left in the bottle when all the doses have been taken.

12 Cambridge is about 350 miles from Glasgow and Brighton is about 240 km from Bristol. Taking 5 miles to equal 8 km, estimate
   a the distance from Cambridge to Glasgow, in kilometres,
   b the distance from Brighton to Bristol, in miles.

13

A man knows that the height of his room is either $2\frac{1}{2}$ m, $3\frac{1}{2}$ m or $4\frac{1}{2}$ m, but he cannot remember which. He can tell, however, that the room is about $1\frac{1}{2}$ times his own height, and he is just under 6 feet tall. Given that 1 foot is about 0·3 m, work out the probable height of the room.

14 Vitamin tablets are sold in bottles which have a mass of 40 g and contain 140 tablets, each with a mass of 250 mg. Work out

a the total mass in grams of one full bottle of the tablets,

b the number of tablets which must be used to reduce the total mass to 58·5 g.

Given that each of the tablets occupies 0·6 ml of space, and $\frac{4}{5}$ of the total capacity of a bottle is occupied when it contains 140 tablets, work out

c the total capacity of a bottle, in millilitres.

Exercise 14B

1 Say which of the units **grams**, **milligrams**, **kilograms** or **tonnes** would be most suitable for measuring each of the following:

a the mass of a ruler,

b the mass of a train,

c your own weight,

d the weight of a feather,

e the load which could be supported by a floor,

f the amount of flour needed to make a cake.

2 Which of the following is nearest to the capacity of an ordinary bathroom washbasin:

a 1500 ml? **b** 50 litres? **c** 1000 cl? **d** 3 litres?

3 The nail and the picture on the left are reproduced to the same scale. Given that the nail is actually 3 cm long, estimate

a the width of the picture,

b the length of the picture.

4 On a small bridge there are cars of mass 1500 kg, $2\frac{1}{2}$ t and 3200 kg, and 8 people with an average mass of 65 kg. The bridge can safely support a load of 25 t. Work out

a the total mass now on the bridge, in tonnes,

b the extra mass that the bridge could safely hold, in kilograms.

5

A ———————————————————————————— B

The points A and B are 9·6 cm apart. If two points are added to the line in such a way that all four points are equally spaced, how far apart will the points be, in millimetres.

6 A tablespoon holds about 18 ml. How many complete tablespoonsful of honey would you expect to get from a pot containing 0·3 litres?

7

Given that the boy is 4 feet 4 inches tall, estimate the height of
a the door,
b the tree,
c the house.

8 An Indian take-away sells portions of rice in foil containers. On average, the containers weigh 15 g and each one holds about 175 g of rice.
  a Estimate the total weight, to the nearest 100 grams, of seven portions of rice in containers.
  b How many portions would be needed to provide just over 2 kg of rice?

9 A bucket weighs 270 g and has a capacity of $6\frac{1}{2}$ litres. Given that 1 ml of water weighs 1 gram, find the total weight in kilograms of the bucket and its contents when it is three-quarters full of water.

10

The plank is being sawn into an exact number of pieces, all of the same length.
  a Work out by measurement how many pieces similar to the one shown will be obtained.
  b Given that the length of the plank is in fact 5·4 m, work out the length of each piece, in centimetres.

11 A bath holds 320 litres. Initially it is half filled with water, then when the water cools $\frac{1}{20}$ of it is run off and 1200 cl of hot water is added.
a How much water is now in the bath, in litres?
b Given that 1 gallon is about $4\frac{1}{2}$ litres, estimate the number of gallons of water in the bath, giving the answer to the nearest gallon.

12 Mr Campbell, who has entered for the London Marathon, decides to start his training by jogging at least 5 km per day. He is told that his local sports ground has a perimeter of 700 yards, and he knows that 1 foot is about 0·3 metres. Work out
a the approximate perimeter of the sports ground, in metres,
b the minimum number of complete circuits Mr Campbell needs to make to fulfil his training requirements.

13 A pack of 52 playing cards is 1·7 cm thick.
a Work out the thickness of one card, to the nearest tenth of a millimetre.

The cards are sold to shops in packages of total thickness 1·9 cm, and the packages are stacked as shown, in layers of six, in boxes of depth 0.4 m.

b Work out the number of packages that will fit in one box.

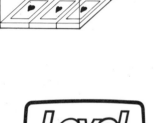

0.4 m

Decimal places, significant figures

Exercise 15A

1 Express to two decimal places:
a 5·342   **b** 0·816   **c** 12·084   **d** 1·298

2 Express to one decimal place:
a 9·21   **b** 17·349   **c** 0·753   **d** $8\frac{2}{3}$

3 Express to two significant figures:
a 847   **b** 0·0324   **c** 1062   **d** 0·5964   **e** 145 704

4 Express to three significant figures:
a 6·231   **b** 12 496   **c** 0·005 013 6   **d** 20·082   **e** 6297

5 Express to one significant figure:
a 473   **b** 0·000 639   **c** twenty-six million

6 The population of a town is 214 700. Express this
a to three significant figures,
b to two significant figures.

State also
c which of these answers gives the population to the nearest thousand people.

7 A garden which is approximately rectangular is 21 m 18 cm long and

15 m 70 cm wide. Estimate the area of the garden, in m²,
a to three significant figures,
b to two decimal places.

State also
c which of the two answers would be the more reasonable estimate to use.

8 To two significant figures, the number of children in a school is 530. Write down
a the smallest possible number of children in the school,
b the largest possible number of children in the school.

9 A woman has to pay bills of £146, £61.09 and £117.80. She wants to know the total bill, to two significant figures.
a Express each of the three bills to two significant figures.
b Add up your answers to **a** and give the total to two significant figures.
c Add up the exact bills and give the total to two significant figures.
d Say which of your last two answers the woman should use as her estimate of the total bill.

10 The area of a square is 15 m². Work out (with a calculator) the length of each side, giving the answer
a to three decimal places,
b to one decimal place.

11 A car travels 300 miles in three days. Given that it travels 75·3 miles on the first day and 102·75 miles on the second, work out how far it travels on the third day, giving the answer
a to one decimal place,
b to three significant figures,
c to one significant figure.

12 To one decimal place, the weight of a bar of chocolate is 82·9 g. Say which one of the following could be the exact weight of the chocolate:
81·89 g, 82·97 g, 83·02 g, 82·86 g.

13 Seventy sheets of paper have a total thickness of 3·56 mm. Estimate the thickness of one sheet of paper in millimetres, giving the answer
a to three decimal places, **b** to three significant figures.

Exercise 15B

1 Express to one decimal place:
a 0·63 **b** 12·28 **c** 5·606 **d** 28·457

2 Express to two decimal places:
a 4·854 **b** 0·899 **c** 17·3649 **d** $2\frac{1}{3}$

3 Express to two significant figures:
a 28·6 **b** 163·84 **c** 12 375 **d** 0·005 27 **e** 646 073

4 Express to four significant figures:
a 12·459 **b** 0·402 138 **c** 160·14 **d** 0·040 719 **e** 54 237 814

5 The diameter of the earth is about 12 740 km. Express this
a to three significant figures, **b** to two significant figures.

State also

c which of these answers gives the diameter to the nearest thousand kilometres.

6 To three significant figures, the total number of runs scored by a cricket team in a season is 11 400. Write down
a the smallest possible number of runs scored by the team,
b the largest possible number of runs scored by the team.

7 The mass of a pin is 0·026 37 g. Express this
a to three significant figures,
b to three decimal places.

State also

c which of these answers gives the mass to the nearest milligram.

8 A boy finds that in 25 ordinary paces he walks a distance of 16 m and 36 cm. Work out the average length in metres of one pace, giving the answer
a to three decimal places,
b to one decimal place.

State also

c which of these answers would be the more reasonable to use as an estimate of the average pace.

9 A nightclub plans to buy 28 chairs at £117 each, and needs to know the total cost to two significant figures.
a Write down the price of one chair to two significant figures.
b Use your answer to **a** to estimate the total cost to two significant figures.
c Work out the exact total cost.
d Express your answer to **c** to two significant figures.
e State which value the nightclub should use as its estimate of the total cost to two significant figures.

10 The population of a country is 20 610 730. How many significant figures are being given when this is expressed
a to the nearest thousand?
b to the nearest hundred thousand?
c to the nearest million?

11 Use your calculator to obtain a value of π, and express this value
a to four significant figures,
b to four decimal places,
c to six significant figures.

12 The capacity of a ketchup bottle is 329 ml to three significant figures. Say which one of the following could be the exact capacity of the bottle:

329·7 ml, 330 ml, 328·57 ml, 327.9 ml

13 The length of a rectangle is 7·3 cm and its area is 31·4 cm². Work out the width of the rectangle, giving the answer
a two decimal places,
b to five significant figures.

Indices, Standard Form

Note: *Do not use a calculator in Exercises 16A and 16B.*

1 Work out:
  a 3^2 **d** 2^{-3} **g** 7^{-2}
  b 3^{-2} **e** 5^4 **h** 2^{-5}
  c 2^3 **f** 5^{-4} **i** 6^{-3}

2 Work out:
  a $\left(\frac{1}{4}\right)^{-2}$ **c** $\left(\frac{2}{3}\right)^{-1}$ **e** $\left(\frac{2}{3}\right)^{-2}$
  b $\left(\frac{1}{3}\right)^{-4}$ **d** $\left(1\frac{1}{4}\right)^{-1}$

3 Work out, expressing the answers as fractions or whole numbers:
  a 0.25^{-1} **c** 0.05^{-2} **e** 0.04^{-2}
  b 0.2^{-2} **d** 0.9^{-1}

4 Work out:

  a 4.23×10 **e** $\dfrac{29.7}{10^3}$ **i** 64.23×10^{-3}

  b 0.708×10^2 **f** 50×10^{-1} **j** 3700×10^{-8}

  c 6.2×10^4 **g** 7×10^{-2}

  d $\dfrac{460}{10^2}$ **h** 0.49×10^{-2}

5 State in words the rules for
  a multiplying a number by 10^n,
  b multiplying a number by 10^{-n}.

6 Express in standard form:
  a 857   **c** 0.000 541   **e** 72 million
  b 0.24   **d** 236 000   **f** 0.000 009

7 Express in standard form:

  a 0.3×10^{-2} **d** $\dfrac{0.0069}{0.3}$ **g** $\dfrac{2}{0.008}$

  b 2600×400 **e** $\dfrac{4 \times 10^5}{2 \times 10^2}$

  c 0.07^2 **f** $\dfrac{6 \times 10^3}{12 \times 10^7}$

8 Express as a power of 2:

a $2^5 \times 2^3$

d $\dfrac{2^{11}}{2^4}$

g $\dfrac{2^9 \times 2^4}{2^5}$

b $2 \times 2^4 \times 2^7$

e $\dfrac{2^2}{2^7}$

h $\dfrac{2^5}{2^7 \times 2^4}$

c $2^x \times 2^y$

f $\dfrac{2^x}{2^y}$

9 Express as a power of 5:

a $5^4 \times 5^{-1}$

c $5^{-3} \times 5^{-2}$

b $5^6 \times 5^{-8}$

d $5^{4x} \times 5^{-8x} \times 5^{-2x}$

10 Express as a power of 3:

a $(3^2)^3$

d 9^4

g $\dfrac{27^4}{9^3}$

b $(3^4)^5$

e 27^5

h $\dfrac{243}{81^4}$

c $(3^x)^y$

f $9^5 \times 81^2$

Exercise 16B

1 Work out:

a 7^2

c 2^{-6}

e 3^{-4}

b 7^{-2}

d 10^{-3}

2 Work out:

a $\left(\frac{1}{3}\right)^{-2}$

c $\left(\frac{2}{5}\right)^{-1}$

e $\left(\frac{3}{4}\right)^{-2}$

b $\left(\frac{1}{2}\right)^{-4}$

d $\left(1\frac{2}{9}\right)^{-1}$

3 Work out, expressing the answers as fractions or whole numbers:

a 0.1^{-1}

c 0.6^{-1}

e 0.05^{-3}

b 0.25^{-2}

d 0.02^{-2}

4 Work out:

a 0.27×10^2

c 5.8×10^4

e 820×10^{-2}

b 0.0069×10^3

d 3×10^{-1}

f 0.72×10^{-3}

5 Express in standard form:

a 9650

d 0.000 02

b 0.053

e 4 684 000

c a quarter of a million

6 Express in standard form:
   a $0{\cdot}02 \times 0{\cdot}003$
   b $0{\cdot}008 \times 10^5$
   c $4 \times 10^2 \times 7 \times 10^4$
   d $\dfrac{0{\cdot}00015}{0{\cdot}05}$
   e $\dfrac{12 \times 10^2}{3 \times 10^8}$
   f $\dfrac{9 \times 10^7}{15 \times 10^3}$

7 Express as a power of 3:
   a $3^6 \times 3^7$
   b $\dfrac{3^{12}}{3^{10}}$
   c $3^{2x} \times 3^{5x}$
   d $\dfrac{3^{7a}}{3^{2a}}$
   e $\dfrac{3 \times 3^6 \times 3^4}{3^7}$
   f $\dfrac{3^5}{3^4 \times 3^{10}}$

8 Express as a power of 7:
   a $7^6 \times 7^{-2}$
   b $7^2 \times 7^{-5} \times 7$
   c $7^{-3} \times 7^{-8}$
   d $7^{-3x} \times 7^{6x} \times 7^{-x}$

9 Express as a power of 2:
   a $(2^4)^2$
   b $(2^x)^5$
   c 8^3
   d 4^7
   e $4^5 \times 32$
   f $8^4 \times 16^3$
   g $\dfrac{16^6}{32^2}$
   h $\dfrac{64}{8^7}$

Time

1   Express the following times in the 24-hour clock notation:

    a 5 a.m.   **d** 9.05 p.m.

    b 4 p.m.   **e** half an hour after 1.55 p.m.

    c 11.24 a.m.   **f** 5 hours before 3.02 p.m.

2   Express the following times in the 12-hour clock notation:

    a 08.20   **d** 23.45

    b 17.00   **e** 50 minutes after 15.40

    c 10.06   **f** 3 hours before 02.30

3   Mrs Ahmed goes out shopping at 11.30 a.m. She has lunch in a restaurant between 1.45 p.m. and 2.20 p.m., carries on shopping, and gets home at 4 p.m.

    a How long does Mrs Ahmed spend at lunch?

    b For how long is she away from home?

    c How long does she spend shopping and travelling?

4   Mr Prior is unemployed from 01–10–83 until 31–7–84. His new job starts on 1–8–84 and lasts for 8 months.

    a For how many months is Mr Prior unemployed?

    b What is the last day of his employment in the new job?

5   The following is an extract from a bus timetable for a Saturday:

Chessington *World of Adventures*	**09**38	**09**49			**17**04	**17**19	**17**34
Copt Gilders Estate	**09**43	**09**54			**17**09	**17**24	**17**39
Surbiton Station ☰ ..✻	**09**58	**10**12	Then	**17**27	**17**42	**17**57
Kingston Station ☰	**10**15	**10**30	every	**17**45	**18**00	**18**15
Kings Road *Park Road*	**10**23	**10**38	15	**17**53	**18**07	**18**22
Ham *Ashburnham Road/Broughton Avenue*	**10**32	**10**47	mins,	**18**02	**18**16	**18**31
Richmond Hill *Star & Garter House*	**10**41	**10**56	until	**18**11	**18**24	**18**39
Richmond Station ⊖☰	**10**52	**11**07			**18**22	**18**33	**18**48
Richmond *Dee Road*	**10**56	**11**11			**18**26	**18**36	**18**51

© London Regional Transport, 1988

    a How long does the first bus take to travel from Chessington 'World of Adventures' to Kings Road?

    b How long does the last bus take to travel from Chessington 'World of Adventures' to Kings Road?

    c A woman arrives at the Surbiton Station stop at 10.15. How long does she have to wait for a bus?

    d She catches the bus and gets off at Kings Road. How long does she spend on the bus?

    e Another woman gets to the Chessington 'World of Adventures' stop at 16.15. At what time does her bus arrive and how long does it take to reach Kingston Station?

    f A man leaving a football match just misses the 18.11 bus from Richmond Hill. How long does he have to wait for the next bus?

6   The members of a family leave home for their summer holiday at 18.00 on Friday 24 June, and return at 08.00 on 3 July.

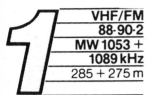

VHF/FM
88-90·2
MW 1053 +
1089 kHz
285 + 275 m

VHF/FM stereo between
10.00pm and 12 midnight
except in the London area,
where you can hear Radio 1 in
stereo all day on VHF/FM 104.8

News on the half hour from
6.30am until 8.30pm,
then 10.00 and 12 midnight

5.30am Adrian John

7.00 Mike Smith's Breakfast Show
Including *Chartbeat*
To vote dial **0898 70086** and
then the number of your choice
from 0 to 9.

9.30 Simon Bates

12.30pm Newsbeat
with **Frank Partridge**

12.45 Gary Davies

3.00 Steve Wright

5.30 Newsbeat
with **Frank Partridge**

5.45 The Best and Worst of Singled Out
Mike Read features some of the
year's most accurate and
outrageous predictions.
Producer CHRIS VEZEY

(Reproduced with
permission from the
Radio Times)

a On what day of the week do they return?
b How long are they away, in days and hours?

7   Start   Finish

The clocks show the starting and finishing times of a journey which
begins in the morning and ends in the afternoon of the same day. How
long does the journey last, in hours and minutes?

8 A train is due to arrive at Euston Station at 15.43, but it is delayed by
half an hour.
a Using the 24-hour clock notation, state the time of the train's arrival.

The following week the train is again delayed, but it makes up 12
minutes on the rest of the journey and arrives at 4.09 p.m.
b Work out the time for which the train is delayed.

9 Some of the programmes for Radio 1 on Monday 26 April are shown
on the left.
a How long is 'Mike Smith's Breakfast Show'?
b 'The Best and Worst of Singled Out' lasts for 50 minutes. At what
time does it finish?
c Mark turns on his radio at the start of Simon Bates' programme,
turns it off for Newsbeat, then listens to Gary Davies and half of
Steve Wright's programme. For how long does he listen altogether?
d 'The Best and Worst of Singled Out' is repeated on the Wednesday
of the following week. What date is this?

Exercise 17B

1 Express the following times in the 24-hour clock notation:
   a 2.30 a.m.   **d** 11.08 p.m.
   b 7 p.m.   **e** $3\frac{1}{2}$ hours after 10.20 a.m.
   c 4.26 a.m.   **f** 40 minutes before 1.10 p.m.

2 Express the following times in the 12-hour notation:
   a 15.00   **d** 04.07
   b 10.14   **e** 35 minutes after 09.45
   c 21.17   **f** 70 minutes before 17.40

3 A school opens at 8.50 a.m. and closes at 3.40 p.m. Morning break lasts from 10.55 a.m. until 11.15 a.m. and the lunch break is from 12.50 p.m. until 2 p.m.
   a How long is the complete school day, including breaks?
   b What is the total length of the two breaks?
   c How much time is available each day for teaching?

4 In a certain year 25 March falls on a Friday. Say which days of the week the following dates fall on:
   a 20 March   **c** 1 April
   b 9 March   **d** 19 April

5 The following is an extract from a bus timetable:

Wallington *Shotfield*	**1140**		00	20	40		**1500**	**1515**	**1532**	**1552**
Wallington Station ⇌	**1142**	Then	02	22	42		**1502**	**1517**	**1534**	**1554**
Hackbridge Corner	**1149**	at	09	29	49		**1509**	**1524**	**1543**	**1603**
Carshalton *Wrythe Green*	**1153**	these	13	33	53		**1513**	**1528**	**1547**	**1607**
Green Wrythe Lane *Thornton Road*	**1157**	minutes	17	37	57 UNTIL		**1517**	**1532**	**1552**	**1612**
St. Helier *Rose*	**1202**	past	22	42	02		**1522**	**1538**	**1558**	**1618**
Sutton Green	**1206**	each	26	46	06		**1526**	**1542**	**1602**	**1622**
Sutton *High Street/Cheam Road*	**1211**	hour	31	51	11		**1531**	**1547**	**1607**	**1627**
Cheam Village Broadway	**1218**		38	58	18		**1538**	**1554**	**1614**	**1634**
North Cheam *Queen Victoria*	**1223**		43	03	23		**1543**	**1559**	**1619**	**1639**
Worcester Park Station ⇌	....		....	....	....			**1605**	**1625**	**1645**

© London Regional Transport, 1988

   a How long does the first bus take to travel from Hackbridge Corner to Sutton Green?
   b A woman gets to the Carshalton stop at 12.15. By how much does she miss a bus and how long does she have to wait for the next one?
   c The bus which is due at St. Helier just before 4 p.m. is 5 minutes late. At what time does it arrive?
   d Mrs Lynch wants to go from Sutton High Street to North Cheam, but she just misses the 15.31 bus and the next one is cancelled. At what time does she catch her bus?
   e From the time at which she arrives at the Sutton High Street bus stop, how long does it take Mrs Lynch altogether to get to North Cheam?

6 Annie and Nick want to watch a TV programme which starts in 20 minutes. Together they spend 5 min 20 s washing up, 3 min 25 s making the beds and 7 min 37 s dusting.
   a How long do they spend working?
   b How much time is left before the programme starts?

7 Hannah has her tenth birthday on 28 September 1986, and her brother Marvin, who is almost 3 years older, has his birthday exactly 2 weeks later.
   a In what year was Marvin born?
   b What is Marvin's birthday?
   c When Marvin is exactly 15 years old, how old will Hannah be, in years and weeks?

8 Rebecca starts her homework at 19.07 and finishes it at 21.02.
   a How long does the homework take?
   b If Rebecca has allowed herself $2\frac{1}{4}$ hours for the work, how much spare time has she gained by finishing it early?

9 Keith goes to bed at 22.43, falls asleep at 23.08, wakes up at 06.50 and gets up at 07.13. When he is not asleep he listens to the radio.
 a For how long is Keith in bed altogether?
 b For how long is he listening to the radio?

10 The following is an extract from a school calendar:

Wed 10 Sept:	Term starts
Thurs 9 Oct:	Open day
Fri 24 Oct:	School closes for half-term
Mon 3 Nov:	School re-opens
Mon 8 Dec.–	
Fri 12 Dec:	Examinations
Fri 19 Dec:	Term ends

 a How many **complete** school weeks are there before half-term?
 b How many school weeks are there between half-term and the examinations?
 c The deputy headmistress starts planning for Open Day on Monday 22 September. How many school days are available for her to spend on it? (Do not count Open Day itself.)
 d Towards the end of term a teacher makes the remark that 'after today there are only 12 school days left'. Work out the date of the day on which he says this, including the day of the week.

Ratio and Proportion

1 Express the following ratios as simply as possible:
   - **a** 4:8
   - **b** 4:6
   - **c** 12:9
   - **d** 25:10
   - **e** 14:35
   - **f** 2:6:10
   - **g** 9:12:21
   - **h** 20:25:100
   - **i** 25 cm to 1 m
   - **j** $1\frac{1}{2}$ kg to 500 g
   - **k** 8 mm to 2 cm
   - **l** £2.70 to 60p

2 A gardener makes up a mixture consisting of 2 parts of peat to 1 part of sand.
   - **a** How much sand should he use with 5 buckets of peat?
   - **b** When he uses 6 litres of sand, how much of the mixture will he make?
   - **c** How much sand will 15 pots of the mixture contain?

3 One evening Mario plays 16 games of darts with his friend Arthur, and wins 10 of them.
   - **a** What is Mario's ratio of wins to losses, expressed as simply as possible?
   - **b** Over a certain weekend Arthur wins 18 games. If the ratio stays the same, how many games does Mario win?

4 The following are the ingredients in a recipe for four portions of braised steak:

Braised Steak *(serves 4)*

2 onions

4 oz mushrooms

3 tablespoons flour

1½ lb chuck steak

   - **a** Work out the ingredients needed for six portions of the braised steak.
   - **b** If 12 oz of mushrooms are used, how much chuck steak will be needed?
   - **c** If half an onion is used, how many portions wil be obtained?

5 Christina divides the time she spends on history, English and science homework in the ratio 2:3:4. One evening Christina spends 40 minutes on science. Work out how long she spends
a on history,
b on English.

Over the whole of one month Christina spends 6 hours on English. Work out how long she spends
c on history,
d altogether on the three subjects.

6 In a map of London, 2 km is represented by 5 cm.
a Work out, as a decimal, what distance is represented by 1 cm.
b On the map, two Underground stations are 12 cm apart. What is their true distance apart?
c On the map, a road is represented as 3·2 cm long. What is its true length?
d A hospital and a school are in fact 7 km apart. How far apart will they be shown on the map?

7 Some of the fines charged by a library for overdue books are shown in the following table:

Days overdue	1	2	3	4	5	6	7
Fine		8p			20p		28p

a Do the fines and the days overdue appear to be in proportion?
b Assuming that the fines and the days overdue **are** in proportion, work out the fines which should go in the spaces.

8 Three workmen take 1 h 12 min to do a certain job. Assuming that all men work equally quickly, work out how long the job would take if done by
a 6 men,
b 1 man,
c 2 men.

9 A model is made of a house on a scale of 2:25.
a In the model, the kitchen is 32 cm long. How long is the real kitchen?
b The real house is 15 m high. How high is the model, in cm?

10 Say in each of the following cases whether the table indicates that the two quantities are in direct proportion, in inverse proportion, or neither:

a

1	2	3	4
5	10	15	20

b

10	12	14	16
5	7	9	11

c

1	2	5	10
100	50	20	10

d

50	40	25	5
4	5	7	40

e

200	150	100	50
2	1·5	1	0·5

f

120	60	20	15
20	40	120	160

11 When a group of people hire a coach, the cost each person pays is inversely proportional to the number of people in the group.

For a certain trip, a group of 12 people have to pay £4 each. Work out how much each person would pay if the group contained
a 24 people,
b 6 people,
c 30 people.

On another trip, a group of 20 people have to pay £6.60 each. Work out how much each person would pay if the group contained

d 5 people,
e 60 people,
f 25 people.

12

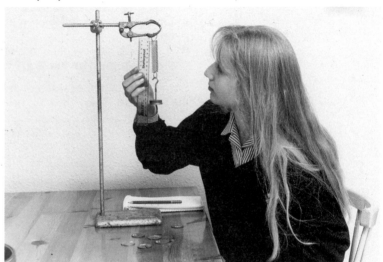

An experiment is performed in which weights are hung on the end of a spring and the extensions of the spring are measured. The results are as follows:

Weight	250 g	500 g	1 kg	$1\frac{1}{2}$ kg	2 kg
Extension	0·6 cm	1·2 cm	2·4 cm	2·6 cm	4·8 cm

a Which extension in the table appears to be a mistaken reading and what would be the correct extension?
b What would be the extension caused by a weight of $1\frac{1}{4}$ kg?
c What weight would produce an extension of 4·2 cm?

Exercise 18B

1 Express the following ratios as simply as possible:
a 2:6 **d** $1\frac{1}{2}$:$2\frac{1}{2}$ **g** 35 cl to 0·5 litres
b 12:8 **e** 7:21:28 **h** 0·2 t to 160 kg
c 25:55 **f** 45:27:18 **i** 6 km to 200 m

2 An alloy is made by mixing copper and tin in the ratio 4:1 by weight.
   a If 220 g of copper is used, how much tin will be needed?
   b When 4 kg of tin is used, how much of the alloy will be obtained?
   c What weight of tin will be needed to make 30 kg of the alloy?

3 Jason is 15 years old and his sister Betty is 5 years older.
   a What is the ratio of Jason's age to Betty's age?
   b What will be the ratio of their ages in 10 years' time?
   c How old will Jason be when the ratio is 9:10?

4 The following are the ingredients in a recipe for 12 small cherry cakes:

Cherry Cakes (*makes 12*)

8 oz flour
5 oz glacé cherries
4 oz sugar
6 oz butter
3 eggs

   a Work out the amounts of flour, sugar and butter that would be needed to make 30 cakes.
   b If one egg were used, how much sugar would be needed?
   c If $2\frac{1}{4}$lb of flour were used, how many cakes would be obtained and how much butter would be needed?

5 In a map of England, 2 inches represent 125 miles.
   a On the map, Hollyhead and Norwich are 5 inches apart. What is their true distance apart, to the nearest 10 miles?
   b Hull is 400 miles from Inverness. How far apart will these towns be shown on the map?
   c On the map, Oxford and Edinburgh are 5·8 inches apart. What is their true distance apart, to the nearest 10 miles?

6 Owen has a part-time job in a hamburger restaurant and divides his earnings between travelling expenses, savings and spending in the ratio 1:4:5.
   a Owen's travelling expenses for a week are £1.20. How much does he earn in a week?
   b Over a certain period Owen saves £160. How much does he spend in that period?
   c In order to save £240, how much must Owen earn?

7 A department store keeps a record of the number of bedside lamps it sells and the number of days it is open:

Days open	20	30	40	50	60
Bedside lamps			600		

Work out the numbers which will go in the spaces if the number of bedside lamps is proportional to the number of days open.

8 A car takes 90 minutes to do a certain journey. Work out how long the car would take to do the same journey if it travelled
a three times as fast,
b one-quarter as fast,
c $4\frac{1}{2}$ times as fast.

9 A small engineering firm employs three grades of workers, namely supervisors, skilled operatives and trainees. They are paid in the ratio 3:2:1.
a One week a supervisor is paid £180. What does a trainee receive?
b A skilled operative earns £650 in March. What does a supervisor earn in the same month?
c The firm puts one supervisor in charge of five trainees and pays her an annual wage of £10 500. What is its total annual wage bill for the five trainees?

10 A carpenter makes a scale drawing of a piece of furniture which he is designing, letting 20 cm represent $1\frac{1}{2}$ m.
a Express the ratio of lengths in the drawing to real lengths as simply as possible.
b In the drawing, the piece of furniture is 8·5 cm wide. What will be its real width?
c The carpenter plans to make the piece of furniture 1·86 m high. Work out the height in the drawing, in cm and mm.

11 Say in each of the following cases whether the table indicates that the two quantities are in direct proportion, in inverse proportion, or neither:

a

2	3	6	10
18	28	56	90

d

1	5	8	12
3	15	24	36

b

80	40	20	10
2	4	8	16

e

5	6	7	8
1	2	3	4

c

3	5	10	20
100	60	30	15

f

1	10	15	40
2	20	35	80

12 A firm which manufactures motorcycles finds that the average number of minor faults in a new motorcycle is inversely proportional to the time that is spent in checking each one.
   One month the firm allows 30 minutes for checking each motorcycle, and the average number of faults is 24. Work out how

many faults would have been likely to have occurred if the time allowed had been

a 2 hours,

b 20 minutes,

c 45 minutes.

Work out also

d the checking time which would have been likely to produce an average of 10 faults per motorcycle.

Proportional division

1 £60 is divided between Sharmilla and Hanif in such a way that Sharmilla receives 2 shares and Hanif receives 3 shares.

a Work out the value of one share.

b Work out the amounts that Sharmilla and Hanif receive.

2 £45 is divided among two people in the ratio 1:2. Work out the amounts they receive.

3 Divide

a 12 in the ratio 1:3

b 25 in the ratio 3:2

c 21 in the ratio 4:3

d 20 in the ratio 1:2:2

e 42 in the ratio 2:1:3

f 80 in the ratio 5:3:2

4 The workers in an electronics factory are given 4 minutes resting time for every 20 minutes they spend working.

a What fraction of their time do the workers spend resting?

b What fraction of their time do they spend working?

c In a 42-hour week, how long do they spend working?

5 One evening Andrea divides her homework time between English, maths and other subjects in the ratio 3:2:7. She spends 1 h 48 min altogether on her homework.

a What fraction of her time does Andrea spend on English?

b What fraction of her time does she spend on maths?

c How long does she spend on maths?

d How long does she spend on subjects other than English or maths?

Over a certain weekend Andrea has to do French, geography and chemistry homework, and she divides her time between them in the ratio 4:3:6. Given that she spends 10 minutes more on French than geography, work out

e how long she spends altogether on homework,

f how long she spends on chemistry.

6 An alloy consists of copper, zinc and tin in the ratio 5:2:1 by weight.
  a How much copper will be contained in 120 kg of the alloy?
  b Find the weight of a piece of the alloy in which there is 9 kg more copper than zinc.

7 Three young children receive pocket money of 25p, 40p and 60p each week. When they are a little older their parents raise the total amount of pocket money to £4, but decide to keep the ratio of the three amounts the same. Work out the three new amounts.

8 A cricket team plays 45 games in a season, achieving wins, losses and draws in the ratio 3:2:4.
  a Work out the numbers of wins, losses and draws.

The following season the team plays the same number of games, but wins three fewer. The ratio of losses to draws stays the same.
  b Work out the numbers of wins, losses and draws for the second season.

Exercise 19B

1 For every £3 that a man leaves to his wife in his will, he leaves £1 to his son. He leaves £20 000 altogether. Work out
  a what fraction of the money the son receives,
  b the amounts received by the son and the wife.

2 Thirty pounds is divided among two people in the ratio 1:5. Work out the amounts they receive.

3 Divide
  a 24 in the ratio 2:1
  b 40 in the ratio 3:5
  c £2.10 in the ratio 5:2
  d £1.32 in the ratio 1:2:3
  e 96 in the ratio 4:3:5
  f 72 in the ratio 1:2:2:3

4 A journey of 220 miles is covered by coach and train, the distances travelled by each being in the ratio 2:9. Work out the distance covered by train.

5 One week three men earn, respectively, £150, £180 and £120.
  a Work out the ratio of their earnings, as simply as possible.

Over a period of several months the three men earn a total of £3000.
  b Assuming that the ratio of their earnings remains the same, work out the men's individual earnings for the period.

6 Half of the books in Carlo's bookcase are on photography, and one-third of the rest are on keep-fit. All the remaining books are novels.
  a Work out the ratio of the number of books on keep-fit to the number of novels.
  b Work out the ratio of the number of books on photography to the number of books on keep-fit to the number of novels.
  c Given that the bookcase contains 60 boots altogether, work out the number of novels it contains.

7 A road 55 miles long has three roundabouts which divide its length in the ratio 2:1:3:4. Work out the distance between the second and third roundabouts.

8 Lisa has some reggae records and some soul records, the numbers being in the ratio 5:9. If Lisa has 40 more soul records than she has reggae records, what is the total number of records in her collection?

9 In a local election the votes received by the Labour, Liberal, Conservative and Independent candidates are in the ratio 6:2:4:1.
  a If the Labour candidate's majority over the Conservative candidate is 3500, how many people voted altogether?
  b If 650 parliamentary seats were divided up in the ratio of the votes cast in the above election, how many seats would each party receive?

Rate

1 A man normally spends 45p per day on bus fares. How much will he
   spend on fares in
   a 5 days?
   b 27 days?

2 A footballer scores, on average, one goal in every four games he
   plays.
   a How many goals can he expect to score in 48 games?
   b In how many games can he expect to score 76 goals?

3 Meryl earns a wage of £75 per week. Work out how much she earns in
   a 8 weeks,
   b 17 weeks,
   c a year.

   Work out also the time for which Meryl needs to work in order to earn
   d £300,
   e £1050,
   f £2175.

4 Simon's normal walking speed is 1·5 m/s. Work out how far he will
   normally walk in
   a 20 seconds,
   b 10 minutes,
   c half an hour.

   Work out also how long Simon will normally take to walk
   d 24 m,
   e 570 m,
   f 3 km.

5 A car uses 2·3 gallons of petrol in travelling 85 miles on a motorway.
   a Work out, to the nearest whole number, how many miles per gallon
      the car is doing.

   The car has 5·7 gallons left in its tank.
   b Assuming that its petrol consumption stays the same, work out, to
      the nearest mile, how many more miles the car can travel before
      running out of petrol.

6 The population of a country is increasing at an average rate of 38
   people per day.
   a Work out, to the nearest 100, how much the population will increase
      by in two years.
   b Work out, to the nearest day, how long the population will take to
      increase by 5000.

7 At her top speed, a journalist can type 325 words in 5 minutes.
   a Work out her maximum rate of typing, in words per minute.

b Work out the maximum number of words she can type in a quarter of an hour.

Normally she works at $\frac{4}{5}$ of her top speed. Working at this speed, she types out a news article containing 1247 words.
c How long does this take, to the nearest minute?

8 Andrew is going on holiday to Spain and needs to change some English pounds into pesetas. The exchange rate is 206 pesetas to the pound.
a How many pesetas will Andrew obtain for £125.50?

When he returns to England, Andrew has 827 pesetas to convert back to pounds. The exchange rate is now 209 pesetas to the pound.
b How much English money does he obtain, to the nearest penny?

9 A train travelling at a steady speed covers $5\frac{1}{4}$ km in 150 seconds.
a Work out the train's speed, in metres per second.

The train travels at this speed for half an hour.
b Work out the distance it covers, in kilometres.

10 A bath has a capacity of 430 litres. The hot water tap is turned on and in $6\frac{1}{2}$ minutes the bath is filled to half its total capacity.
a Work out the rate at which the tap delivers water, giving the answer in litres per minute to the nearest whole number.

When the half-filled bath is emptied, the water runs out at an average rate of 0·85 litres per second.
b Work out the time it takes the bath to empty, giving the answer in minutes and seconds to the nearest second.

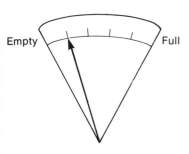

Empty   Full

11 The diagram on the left shows the petrol gauge of a car whose tank can hold 6 gallons of petrol. The car does an average of 27 miles to the gallon and the driver does not like to risk having less than half a gallon in the tank.
Estimate to the nearest mile how far the car can travel before the driver needs to fill up.

12 Jim Highgate, a best-selling author, sets out to write three pages of his new book every day except on Saturdays and Sundays. The pages contain, on average, 340 words each. Work out
a how many pages Jim plans to write in 4 weeks,
b how many words he plans to write per week.

The book will eventually contain about 90 000 words. Work out
c how many weeks altogether it is likely to take Jim to write the book, giving the answer to the nearest whole number.

13 A car travels 150 miles at an average speed of 50 miles per hour, then travels for two hours at 60 miles per hour.
a How far does the car travel altogether?
b How long does the complete journey take?
c What is the average speed for the complete journey?

1 A man smokes 14 cigarettes per day.
  a How many cigarettes does he smoke in the whole of June?
  b In how many days does he smoke 322 cigarettes?

2 A car covers 184 km in 4 hours. Work out
  a the car's averge speed, in km/h,
  b how far the car will travel, at this average speed, in $7\frac{1}{2}$ hours.

3 A woman drinks, on average, one cup of tea every 3 hours.
  a How many cups of tea will she normally drink in a week?
  b In how many days will she normally drink 240 cups of tea?

4 In a mathematics test consisting of 40 short questions, Belinda answers the questions at a rate of 0·5 questions per minute. If she is allowed $1\frac{1}{2}$ hours for the test, how long will Belinda have left at the end for checking?

5 Mrs O'Neill finds that in 423 km of town driving, her car uses 45 litres of petrol. Work out
  a the average number of kilometres per litre that Mrs O'Neill is getting from her car.

On five days of each week Mrs O'Neill drives to and from her office, which is 12·5 km from her home. Work out
  b how many litres of petrol she will normally use per week, to the nearest litre.

6 A long-distance runner trains by running at a steady speed of 5 m/s. Work out the distance in metres he will run in
  a 1 minute,
  b 1 hour.

By converting your answer to **b** into kilometres, work out
  c the runner's speed in km/h.

One day the runner maintains his normal training speed for 45 minutes, then jogs at half this speed for 20 minutes. Work out
  d how far he runs altogether, in kilometres.

7 A bakery uses 225 g of flour and 130 g of sugar to produce each swiss roll. Work out
  a the weight in kilograms of flour and of sugar needed to make 2500 swiss rolls;
  b the number of swiss rolls that can be made with 189 kg of flour, and the amount of sugar that will be needed for them.

8 A visitor to Australia receives 624 dollars for £260. Work out
  a the exchange rate, in dollars per pound,
  b the amount of Australian money that would be obtained for £430,
  c the amount of English money, to the nearest penny, that would be obtained for 500 dollars.

9 A pipe delivers 250 litres of water per minute to a tank with a capacity of 4650 litres. How long will the pipe take to fill the tank, in minutes and seconds?

10 A theatre's prices for tickets are as set out in the following table:

IRVING THEATRE Seat Prices			
	low rate	**middle rate**	**peak rate**
Stalls	£9	£10.50	£13.50
Lower gallery	£7	£8.50	£11
Upper gallery	£5.50	£6.50	£8.50

The peak rate is charged for the months of May to August inclusive, the low rate for the months of November to February inclusive, and the middle rate for the other months. There are no reduced rates for children.

a A man wants to take his wife and two children to see *Julius Caesar* on 18 September. How much will this cost if he books tickets in the stalls?

b A party of 20 children pays a total of £110 to see a performance of *Peter Pan*. Do they go in the winter or the summer, and where do they sit?

c A woman books two tickets for *The Phantom of the Opera* for 25 April, but has to cancel and re-book for a fortnight later. The new tickets, which are for the same seats, cost an extra £5. What is the position of the seats?

11 I walk at 2 m/s for 2 minutes, then jog at 3 m/s for 3 minutes.

a How far do I travel altogether?

b What is my average speed for the whole journey, in m/s?

12 A solicitors' office makes an average of 40 telephone calls per hour. The office works a 7-hour day and a 5-day week. Work out

a the average number of telephone calls made by the office per week,

b the time normally taken, in weeks and days to the nearest day, for the office to make 5000 calls.

The calls cost, on average, 6·4p each. Work out

c the office's average weekly telephone bill,

d the approximate time it takes, in hours to the nearest whole number, for the office to spend £50 on telephone calls.

Graphs

Practical graphs

1   The following graph shows how the height of a growing plant
    increases over a period of 50 days:

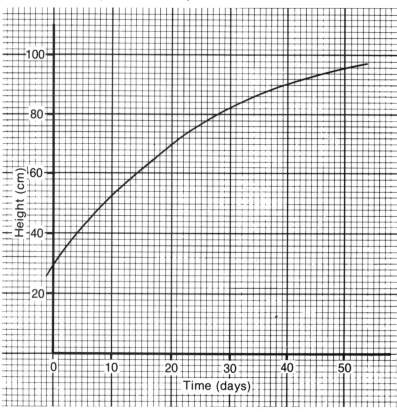

Read off from the graph, as accurately as possible,
a the height of the plant on the 10th day,
b the day on which the height is 34 cm,
c the height of the plant on the 46th day,
d the day on which the height is 74 cm,
e the time it takes for the plant to grow from 60 cm to 90 cm.

2   The following conversion graph relates kilograms and pounds:

Use the graph to find, to the nearest whole number,
a the weight in kilograms of a girl who weighs 82 lb,
b the weight in pounds of a chair which weighs 8 kg,
c the total weight in kilograms of four articles weighing 16 lb each,
d the total weight in pounds of three articles weighing 7·3 kg each.

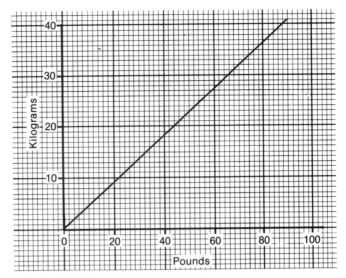

3 A manufacturing firm finds that the time taken to make a certain product varies with the number of people working on the product as shown in the following table:

Number of people	5	10	15	20	25	30
Time taken	76	70	62	50	44	34

Draw a scatter diagram to represent these data on graph paper, letting 2 cm represent 5 people and letting 2 cm represent 20 days. Draw a line of best fit and use it to estimate
a the time that would be taken if 8 people were working,
b the number of people that would take 40 days to make the product.

4

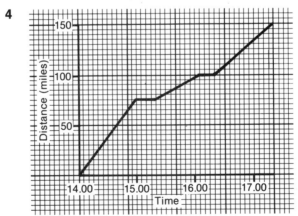

The above graph represents the journey of a train which travels 150 miles altogether and stops at two stations. Work out
a how long the train spends at each station,
b how far apart the stations are,
c the speed of the train on the first stage of its journey,
d the time at which it starts the final stage of its journey,
e its speed on the final stage of its journey,
f how long it spends in motion altogether.

5 From the following table construct a conversion graph relating English pounds and French francs:

Pounds	1·4	2·6	3·7
Francs	15	28	40

Use the graph to convert
a £3.50 to francs, to the nearest whole number,
b 23 francs to pounds and pence, to the nearest 10p.

6 The following table shows a car's petrol consumption at various steady speeds:

Speed (miles per hour)	20	30	38	55	70	80
Miles per gallon	33	40	43	42	32	22

Represent the above data as a series of points on graph paper and draw as smooth a curve as possible through the points. Use the graph to estimate
a the maximum number of miles per gallon that can be obtained, and the speed at which this occurs,
b the two speeds at which the car does 35 miles to the gallon.

7 A cyclist, a car driver and a runner each make the same 20 km journey, starting at the same time. The three journeys are represented by the travel graphs shown below.

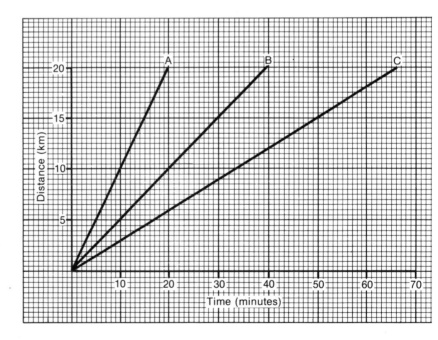

a Say which line represents which traveller and work out the speed of each.

b Work out the difference between the time taken by the runner and the time taken by the cyclist for the complete journey.

c When the car is at the halfway point, how far ahead of the runner is it?

Five minutes after completing the 20 km journey, the car is driven back to its starting point at constant speed, arriving exactly 1 hour after it originally set out. Work out

d the time at which the car passes the cyclist and their distance from the starting point at this time.

8   The charges made by a car-hire company for renting a small car for a day are shown in the following table:

Distance covered in miles	0	50	100	150	200
Cost in pounds	30	40	50	60	70

Draw a graph of distance against cost and use the graph to work out
a the cost of hiring a car and driving it 115 miles,
b the distance which can be covered for £48.

The cost of hiring a car can be considered to be made up of a standing charge and a charge of a certain amount per mile driven. Work out
c the standing charge,
d the charge per mile.

Another company makes a standing charge of £10 and charges 40p per mile for the same type of car. On the same graph paper draw the graph of distance against cost for this case and work out
e the distance for which the two companies charge the same amount.

9   The table below shows the numbers of pages and the weights of some of the books in certain series of paperbacks.

Number of pages	80	170	290	410	530	690
Weight (grams)	60	120	185	260	335	430

Represent the data on a scatter diagram, letting 2 cm represent 100 pages and letting 4 cm represent 100 g. Draw a line of best fit and use it to estimate
a the weight of a book containing 500 pages,
b the number of pages in a book weighing 370 g,
c the increase in weight which results from adding 50 pages to a book.

10   The percentage of men unemployed in a certain city is measured at the beginning of every other year. The results for the years 1978 to 1988 are shown in the following graph.

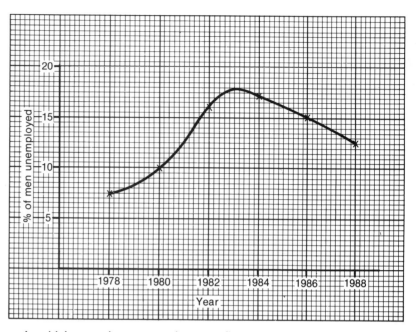

a In which year does unemployment first begin to fall?

b In which year does the greatest rise in unemployment occur?

Given that the total number of men of working age remains constant over the 10-year period at around 80 000, estimate

c the number of men unemployed at the beginning of 1981,

d the maximum number of men unemployed,

e the number who are likely to be unemployed in 1990.

11 Mehmet and Denise visit each other's towns, which are 40 km apart, on the same afternoon. Their journeys are represented by the two travel graphs below.

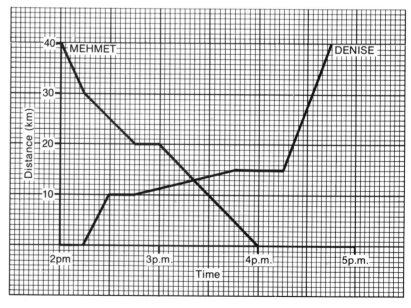

a Which of the two people takes the longer time for the journey, and by how much?

b Estimate the time at which they cross.

c For how long altogether is Denise stationary?

d How far does Mehmet travel while Denise stops for the first time?

e What is the highest speed at which either of the two people travels?

f What is the lowest speed at which either of the two travels?

Exercise 21B

1 The following graph shows how the temperature of a room changes through one night in winter. The room is warmed during the day by central heating, but the heating is turned off at night.

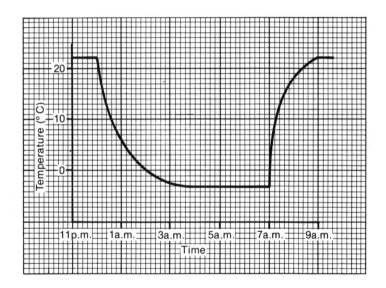

a For how long is the central heating turned off?

b What is the daytime temperature of the room?

c What temperature does the room fall to when the heating is turned off?

d To the nearest 10 minutes, what are the two times at which the temperature is 10°C?

e Approximately how long does the room take to rise from its lowest temperature to 16°C?

f How much does the temperature fall between 1 a.m. and 3 a.m.?

2 The conversion graph below relates inches and centimetres.

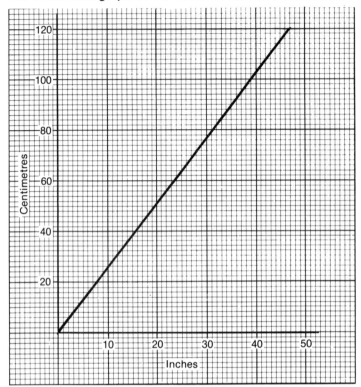

Use the graph to answer the following questions to the nearest whole number.

a A table is 3 feet high. How high is it in centimetres?

b A piece of paper is 54 cm long. How long is it in inches?

c A marble rolls at 44 inches per second. How fast does it roll in centimetres per second?

3 Andy walks from his home to his cousin's house to collect some tapes, chats to her for a few minutes, then walks home, calling in at the newsagent's on the way back. This journey is represented by the following travel graph:

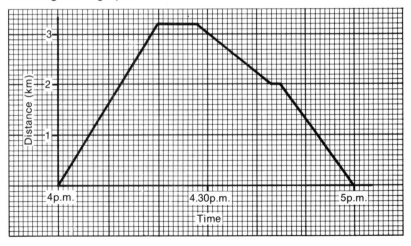

a How far from Andy's home does his cousin live?
b How long does Andy stay with his cousin?
c At what time does he arrive at the newsagent's?
d How long does he take to get from the newsagent's to his home?
e How fast does he walk from the newsagent's to his home, in km/h?
f How fast does he walk to his cousin's house, in km/h?

4   One summer a travel company finds that the number of holidays it sells varies with the prices of the holidays as shown in the following table:

Price of holiday	£50	£120	£200	£280	£350	£430
Number of holidays booked	240	210	190	160	140	120

Display this information in a scatter diagram, letting 2 cm represent £100 and letting 4 cm represent 100 holidays. Draw a line of best fit and use it to estimate
a the number of holidays costing £230 that the company could expect to sell,
b the price of a holiday which would be likely to sell to 200 people,
c the number of people who would be likely to buy a £600 holiday.

5   From the following table draw a conversion graph relating German marks and Danish kroner:

Marks	21	30	42
Kroner	80	114	160

Giving the answers to the nearest whole number, use the graph to convert
a 14 marks to kroner,
b 126 kroner to marks.

6   On August Bank Holiday, the number of people at a funfair varies through a particular day as shown in the following table:

Number of minutes after opening	0	20	50	80	110	150	190	230	290	360	450	600
Number of people at funfair	0	200	400	600	760	960	1080	1160	1160	1080	940	640

Plot this information as a series of points on graph paper. Let the horizontal axis represent time, with a scale of 2 cm to 100 minutes, and let the vertical axis represent the number of people, with a scale of 2 cm to 200 people. Draw as smooth a curve as possible through the points and use the graph to estimate
a the maximum number of people at the funfair, and the time at which this occurs,
b the two times at which there are 820 people at the funfair,
c the increase in the number of people at the funfair in the second hour after it opens,
d the time it takes for the number of people to fall from 1000 to 700.

7   A train leaves Carminster Station at 14.00 and travels at a constant speed to Bankwell Station, which is 90 km away. It arrives at Bankwell at 15.00, stays for 10 minutes then returns at constant speed to

Carminster. On its return journey the trian passes through Stratfield Station, which is 60 km from Carminster, at 15.40.

Draw a travel graph to represent this journey, letting 6 cm represent 1 hour and letting 2 cm represent 20 km.   Work out from the graph
a the time at which the train arrives back at Carminster,
b its speed on the return journey,
c the time interval between the train's two visits to Stratfield Station.

At a distance of 18 km from Bankwell Station there is a level crossing. Work out
d the two times at which the train reaches the crossing.

8 Mr Jarvis owns a hamburger stall. The following table shows how his daily expenses depend upon the number of hamburgers he makes:

Number of hamburgers	8	12	20	32
Expenses	£4	£5.20	£7.60	£11.20

Draw a graph of expenses against the number of hamburgers made and use it to find
a how much Mr Jarvis spends when he makes 16 hamburgers,
b how many hamburgers he can make for £8.80.

Mr Jarvis's expenses are made up of an initial outlay together with a certain cost for each hamburger. Work out
c the initial outlay,
d the additional cost of each hamburger.

Mr Jarvis charges his customers 56p for each hamburger. Using the same graph paper, draw a second graph to represent the money he receives against the number of hamburgers he sells. Work out
e the minimum number of hamburgers Mr Jarvis must sell to make a profit,
f how much profit he makes if he sells 20 hamburgers.

9 The following travel graphs represent the journeys of two cars which are on the same road and are initially moving towards each other.

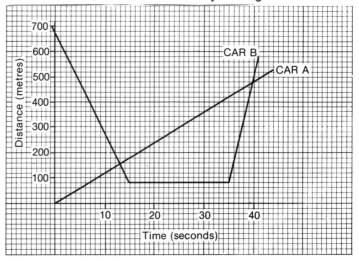

Use the graphs to work out
a the time for which car B is stationary,
b the time interval between the two moments at which the cars are together,
c the speed of car A,
d the initial speed of car B,
e the distance apart of the cars at the moment when car B starts to move in the same direction as car A,
f the distance travelled by car A while car B is stationary.

10 The following table shows how the total weight of a tin of screws varies with the number of screws it contains:

Number of screws	8	24	36	56	70	88
Weight (grams)	22	44	58	80	98	118

Draw a scatter diagram to represent this information, letting 2 cm represent 20 screws and letting 2 cm represent 20 g. Draw a line of best fit and use it to estimate, to the nearest whole number,
a the total weight of the tin and its contents when it contains 76 screws,
b the number of screws in the tin when the total weight is 64 g,
c the weight of the tin alone,
d the weight of one screw.

11 Each of the graphs on the left is of unemployment (on the vertical axis) against time (on the horizontal axis):

In each of the following cases, say which of the graphs (i) to (vi) is being referred to:

a Unemployment is falling at a steady rate.
b Unemployment is rising more and more rapidly.
c Unemployment has been unchanged for some time.
d Unemployment has reached a peak and is now falling.
e Unemployment is falling, but by less and less each month.
f Unemployment is rising, but the rate of increase is going down.

(i) 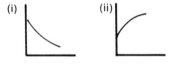 (ii)

(iii) 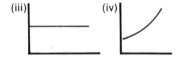 (iv)

(v) 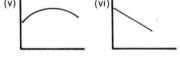 (vi)

Graphs of equations

Level 2

1 Copy and complete the following table for the graph of $y = 2x + 3$.

x	−2	−1	0	1	2	4	6
y				5		11	

Draw the graph, letting 2 cm = 1 unit on the x-axis and letting 1 cm = 1 unit on the y-axis. Find

a the coordinates of the point where the graph meets the x-axis,
b the gradient of the graph,
c a solution of the equation $2x + 3 = 8.6$.

Make a table for the equation $y = 10 - 3x$, letting x have the values 0, 1, 2, 3. Draw a graph of this equation on the same axes as the first graph and find
d the gradient of the second graph,
e the coordinates of the point of intersection of the graphs,
f the solution of the simultaneous equations $y = 2x + 3$, $y = 10 - 3x$.

2 A train is travelling directly away from London. The following table shows how its distance from London varies with time:

Time (hours)	0	1	2	3	4
Distance (km)	50	135	220	305	390

Draw a graph of distance from London against time, using scales of 4 cm to 1 hour and 2 cm to 50 km.
a Read off, to the nearest 10 km, the train's distance from London after 1·3 h, 2·8 h and 3·4 h.
b Write down the train's initial distance from London.
c Work out the gradient of the graph, and say what this represents.
d Write down the equation of the graph, letting d km be the distance from London and t seconds be the time.

3 Without drawing the graphs, work out the coordinates of the points at which the following graphs meet the x-axis and the y-axis:
a $y + 2x = 6$ **d** $4x - 2y + 10 = 0$
b $3y - 2x = 12$ **e** $3 - 10x = 5y$
c $4y = 6 - x$

4 Copy and complete the following table for the graph of $y = 1.2x^2$.

x	−2	−1·5	−1	−0·5	0	0·5	1	1·5	2
y	4·8					0·3			

Draw the graph, taking 4 cm as 1 unit on the x-axis and 2 cm as 1 unit on the y-axis. Work out from the graph, to one decimal place,
a the value of y when $x = 1.8$,
b the two solutions of the equation $1.2x^2 = 3.4$,
c the range of values of x for which $1 < y < 2$.

Draw a tangent to the graph at the point where $x = 0.7$, and hence
d estimate the gradient at this point.

5 Draw on the same axes the graph of $3x + y = 13$, letting $x = 2, 4, 6$, and also the graph of $x + 2y = 8.5$, letting $x = 0.5, 2.5, 4.5$. (Choose appropriate scales yourself.) Hence work out the values of x and y at which the two equations are simultaneously true.

6 A rectangle has a fixed area of 10 m². Given that its width is x m, show that its length, y m, is given by the equation $y = 10/x$.

Make a table for the equation $y = 10/x$ for $0 < x \leqslant 10$. Taking the same scale on each axis, draw the graph of the equation and use it to estimate, to one decimal place,
a the length of the rectangle when its width is 1·7 m,
b the range of values of x for which the length lies between 4·2 m and 6·5 m,
c the value of x for which the rectangle becomes a square.

Draw the line of symmetry of the graph of $y = 10/x$, and
d write down the equation of this line.

7 One car starts with 32 litres of petrol in its tank, while another starts at the same time with 27 litres. The first car uses 7·4 litres per hour and the second uses 5 litres per hour.
Explain why the amounts of petrol, p litres, that the cars have in their tanks after t hours, are given by the equations
$$p = 32 - 7·4t$$
$$p = 27 - 5t$$
Using the same axes, draw the graphs of these equations for values of t from 0 to 3. Read off from the graphs, as accurately as possible,
a the time at which the cars have the same amount of petrol in their tanks, and the amount this is;
b the amounts of petrol the cars have left after 45 minutes;
c the time at which the first car has 2 litres more than the second.

8 Copy and complete the following table for the graph of $y = x^2 - 4x$.

x	-1	-0.5	0	0·5	1	1·5	2	2·5	3	3·5	4	4·5	5
y	5		0	$-1·75$			-4	$-3·75$				2·25	

Draw the graph, letting 2 cm = 1 unit on each axis. Use the graph to estimate, to one decimal place,
a the value of y when $x = 1·3$,
b the two solutions of the equation $x^2 - 4x = 3·4$,
c the minimum value of y,
d the equation of the line of symmetry of the graph.

9 For a certain time the height of a growing plant is given by the formula $h = 8 + \frac{1}{2}t$, where h cm is the height of the plant after t days. Draw the graph of h against t for the range $0 \leqslant t \leqslant 6$.
a Work out the gradient of the graph and say what it represents.

Another plant has a height of 3 cm when $t = 0$, and grows at 2·3 cm per day.
b State the equation relating h and t for the second plant.

On the same axes as the first graph draw the graph of h against t for the second plant, and use the graphs to estimate
c the time at which the plants have the same height, and the value of this height,
d the period of time for which the difference in the plants' heights is more than 1·4 cm.

10 Draw the graph of $y = 9 - x^2$ for the range $-3 \leqslant x \leqslant 3$, taking scales of 2 cm to 1 unit on the x-axis and 1 cm to 1 unit on the y-axis.

a By drawing tangents, estimate the gradients at the points where $x = -2.5$, -0.8 and 0.4.

b Draw the line $y = 7$, and state the coordinates of the points at which it intersects the first graph.

c State the positive solution of the equation $9 - x^2 = 7$, to one decimal place.

d Draw the line $y = x$, and hence find the coordinates of the point on the graph of $y = 9 - x^2$ at which x and y are equal.

1 Make tables for the equations $x + y = 0$ and $x + y = -2$, letting x vary from -2 to $+2$ in each case. Draw the graphs of the equations on the same axes and draw also the graph which passes through the points (0,2) and (2,0).

a State the gradient of all the three graphs.

b Write down the equation of the third graph.

On the same axes draw the graph of the equation $2y = 3x + 5$, letting x have the values -1, 0 and 1. Find:

c the gradient of this graph.

d the solution of the simultaneous equations $2y = 3x + 5$, $x + y = -2$.

2 The following table shows how a man's distance from his house varies with time as he walks away from the house.

Time (seconds)	0	5	10	15	20
Distance (m)	25	34	43	52	61

Draw a graph of distance against time, using scales of 2 cm to 5 seconds and 2 cm to 10 m.

a Read off, to the nearest metre, the man's distance from his house after 6 seconds and after 13 seconds.

b Write down the man's initial distance from his house.

c Work out the gradient of the graph, and say what it represents.

d Write down the equation of the graph, letting d m be the distance and t seconds the time.

The man's wife walks along the same street in the opposite direction, her distance from the house varying with time as follows.

Time (seconds)	0	5	10	15	20
Distance (m)	57	46	35	24	13

Draw the graph of the woman's distance against time on the same axes as the first graph. Find

e the gradient of the second graph,

f the equation of the graph,

g the time at which the man and his wife cross, and their distance from their house at that time.

3 Without drawing the graphs, work out the coordinates of the points at which the following graphs meet the x-axis and the y-axis:

a $3y + x = 12$ **d** $4x + 2y - 1 = 0$
b $y = 2x - 4$ **e** $5x - 10y = 2$
c $6x = y - 9$

4 A pyramid of height $7\frac{1}{2}$ m has a square base of side-length x m. Given that the volume of any pyramid is one third of the area of the base multiplied by the height, show that the volume of the pyramid on the left is given by the formula $V = 2.5x^2$.

Copy and complete the following table for the formula $V = 2.5x^2$.

x	0	0·5	1	1·5	2	2·5	3
V	0	0·6	2·5				

Draw the graph of V against x, using scales of 4 cm to 1 unit on the x-axis and 2 cm to 5 units on the V-axis. Read off, as accurately as possible,
a the volume of the pyramid when $x = 2.2$,
b the value of x for which the volume is 7 m³.

A pyramid has to be made with a base area of at least 4 m² and with a volume that does not exceed 20 m³. Work out
c the range of possible values of x.

5 Draw on the same axes the graphs of $y = 3x - 1$ and $2y = x + 6$, letting x have the values 0, 1, 2 in each case. Hence solve the simultaneous equations $y = 3x - 1$, $2y = x + 6$.

6 For a certain time the population of a country obeys the equation $N = 80 + 12t - t^2$, where N is the population in millions after t years. Draw a graph of N against t, letting t vary from 0 to 7 and starting the N-axis at $N = 70$. Work out
a the population, to the nearest million, after 2·6 years,
b the time in years, to one decimal place, at which the population is 110 million,
c the maximum population.

Draw a tangent to the graph at the point where $t = 3$, and hence find
d the rate of growth of the population after 3 years.

7 Copy and complete the following table for the equation $y = x + \dfrac{1}{x}$:

x	0·25	0·5	0·75	1	1·5	2	2·5	3	4
y	4·25				2·17			3·33	

Draw the graph of the equation, taking scales of 4 cm to 1 unit on the x-axis and 2 cm to 1 unit on the y-axis. Use the graph to estimate, as accurately as possible,
a the value of y when $x = 1.7$,

b the two solutions of the equation $x + \dfrac{1}{x} = 4$,
c the minimum value of y,
d the gradient at the point where $x = 0.5$.

8 The speed of a car is given by the formula $v = 7 + \dfrac{3t}{2}$ where v m/s is the speed after t seconds. Draw a graph of v against t for the range of $0 \leqslant t \leqslant 8$.

    a Another car is travelling at a steady speed of 12·4 m/s. After what time will the two cars have the same speed?

    b Work out the gradient of the graph and say what it represents.

A lorry has a speed of 14 m/s at $t = 0$, and it loses speed at $\frac{3}{4}$ m/s every second.

    c Write down the equation which gives v in terms of t for the lorry.

Draw, on the same axes as the first graph, the graph of v against t for the lorry, and work out

    d the time, to one decimal place, at which the car and the lorry have the same speed.

9 The perimeter of a rectangle is 30 cm. Show that, if the width of the rectangle is x cm, its area is given by the formula $A = x(15 - x)$.

Draw the graph of A against x for $0 \leqslant x \leqslant 15$, taking a scale of 1 cm to 1 unit on the x-axis and 2 cm to 5 units on the A-axis. Find, from the graph, as accurately as possible,

    a the maximum area of the rectangle,

    b the area of the rectangle when $x = 2·8$,

    c the values of x for which the area is 48 cm²,

    d the range of possible values of x, given that the area must be at least 40 cm².

Statistics

1   A factory makes a survey of the number of people who are late for work each day. The results for 1 week are as follows.

Monday	Tuesday	Wednesday	Thursday	Friday
26	15	10	16	18

Monday   人 人 人 人 人

Tuesday

Wednesday

Thursday

Friday

a What is the best day, and what is the worst day, from the factory's point of view?

b Display the above data in the form of a pictogram, as shown on the left. Each individual picture represents five people and the numbers are rounded off to the nearest five.

Work out from the original data

c the total number of people who are late in the whole week,

d the mean number of people who are late each day.

2   One hundred children are asked to name their favourite sport, with the results shown in the bar chart below.

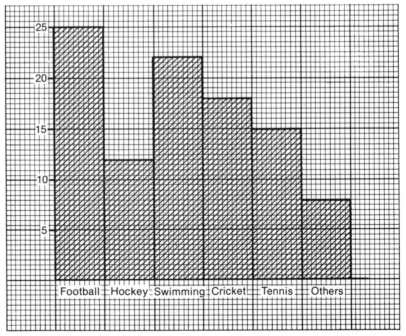

a Copy the following table and use the bar chart to complete it.

Football	Hockey	Swimming	Cricket	Tennis	Others
25					

b Name the most popular sport.
c What fraction of the children chose football?
d What fraction of the children chose tennis?
e If the 100 children form a typical sample, how many children out of a sample of 5000 would be likely to choose football?

3 A cricketer's scores in five innings are 17, 29, 84, 2, 28. Work out
a his mean score,
b the range of his scores.

4 A football team's scores in 15 matches are
$$2, 1, 1, 0, 3, 1, 0, 2, 4, 1, 2, 1, 0, 2, 1$$
a What is the score that occurs most often (the 'mode' of the scores)?
b Arrange the scores in ascending order and say which score is halfway up the list. (This is called the 'median' score.)
c Work out the total score.
d Work out the mean score.
e Work out the range of the scores.

5 Forty students take a test and each is given a mark out of 10. The results are as follows.

$$\begin{array}{cccccccccc}
4, & 5, & 2, & 9, & 6, & 2, & 5, & 8, & 6, & 5, \\
6, & 7, & 4, & 8, & 3, & 7, & 9, & 6, & 3, & 6, \\
10, & 5, & 6, & 1, & 7, & 6, & 0, & 7, & 5, & 7, \\
7, & 6, & 4, & 5, & 10, & 4, & 5, & 6, & 3, & 4
\end{array}$$

a Put the results in the form of a table, as shown below.

Mark	Tally	Frequency
Less than 3	I I I I	4
3	I I I	3
4	IIII I	5
5		
6		
7		
More than 7		

b Show the same information in a bar chart, drawn on graph paper. Take a scale of 1 cm to 1 unit on the vertical axis, and 2 cm to each division on the horizontal axis. Use the horizontal axis for the marks, and the vertical axis for the frequency.
c State the mark that occurred most often (the 'modal' mark).

Find the fraction of the students who got
d less than 3 marks.
e 4 marks.
f 7 marks.

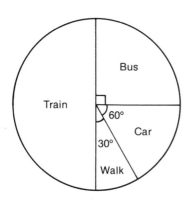

6 Sixty people are asked how they get to work. The results are shown in the pie chart on the left.

Work out how many people go
a by train,
b by bus,
c by car,
d on foot.

State also

e which is the modal form of transport.

7 In the same way as in question **4**, work out the mode, median, mean and range of the following numbers:

3, 4, 2, 3, 2, 4, 8, 5, 5, 7, 3, 4, 5, 3, 2

8 At lunch time, a pub sells ham, cheese and egg sandwiches. Its sales for a particular week are shown in the following table.

	Monday	Tuesday	Wednesday	Thursday	Friday
Ham	8	9	10	10	11
Cheese	10	9	12	11	12
Egg	7	8	6	8	9
Totals	25			29	32

a Work out the totals for Tuesday and Wednesday.
b Name the most popular day of the week and the most popular type of sandwich.
c Work out the total number of sandwiches sold in the week.
d Work out the mean number of sandwiches sold per day.

9 The following pictogram shows the numbers of cars that pass a certain level crossing in each of 4 weeks. The numbers are rounded off to the nearest 250.

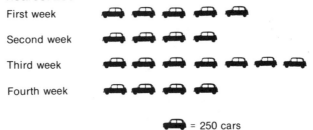

First week

Second week

Third week

Fourth week

= 250 cars

Work out
a the number of cars (to the nearest 250) for each of the 4 weeks,
b the total for the whole 4-week period,
c the mean number of cars using the crossing per week.

10 The mean of two numbers is $13\frac{1}{2}$. If the lower number is 5, what is the higher?

11 The mean age of five women working in a sports shop is 34. If one woman aged 46 joins the shop as a new manageress, what is the mean age of the six women?

12 A bookshelf in a school contains nine copies of a textbook with 170 pages, six copies of a textbook with 238 pages, three dictionaries with 620 pages each and two copies of a novel with 472 pages. The numbers of pages in the other books on the shelf are as follows:

311, 73, 514, 307, 391, 742, 427, 395, 143, 94

a Display this information in the form of a table, as shown below.

Number of pages	Frequency
0–100	
101–200	
201–300	
301–400	
401–500	
Over 500	

b Draw a bar chart of the information, taking 2 cm to each 100-page division on the horizontal axis and 1 cm to 1 unit on the vertical axis.
c What type of book occurs most frequently?
d What fraction of the books have between 201 and 300 pages?
e What fraction of the books have between 301 and 400 pages?

13 One Saturday, ninety people at the Hayfield Shopping Centre are asked their favourite entertainment from the cinema, the theatre, concerts, opera and ballet. The results are shown in the pie chart.

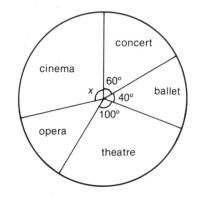

Work out the number that chose
a concerts,
b ballet,
c the theatre.

Given that 30 people chose the cinema, work out
d the angle x,
e the number that chose opera.

Exercise 23B

1 The following table shows the number of houses built each year in a certain town.

1982	1983	1984	1985	1986
313	360	440	346	291

1982
1983
1984
1985
1986

a Display this information in the form of a pictogram, as shown on the left. Each individual diagram represents 50 houses and the numbers are rounded off to the nearest 50.
Work out from the original data
b which was the best of the five years for house building,
c how many more houses were built in the best year than the worst year,

d how many houses were built altogether in the 5-year period,

e the mean number of houses built per year.

2 Marisa spends her wages, in a typical week, as shown in the following bar chart.

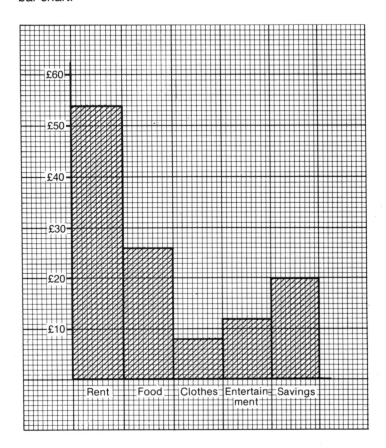

a Copy the following table and use the bar chart to complete it.

Rent	Food	Clothes	Entertainment	Savings
£54				

b Work out her total weekly wage.

Work out the fraction of her wages that Marisa uses for

c entertainment,

d savings,

e clothes.

3 Temperatures are recorded at a certain place at regular intervals. The results are as follows:

$$5°C, \ 2°C, \ -3°C, \ 4°C, \ -1°C, \ 7°C, \ 5°C, \ 9°C$$

Work out

a the range of the temperatures,

b the mean temperature.

4 The time in minutes that Karen takes to drive to the supermarket is recorded each time for 11 visits. The results are as follows:

31, 35, 33, 33, 30, 32, 31, 33, 30, 33, 31

a State the mode (most frequent) of the times.
b Arrange the times in ascending order and state the median time.
c Work out the mean time.
d Work out the range of the times.

5 The following are the numbers of days of absence of each of the members of a school class in a particular year:

```
5,  0,  8,  6,  7,  1,  9,  4,
9,  6, 12,  7, 17, 10,  7, 25,
7,  8, 10,  9,  0,  8,  6,  7,
6,  4,  7,  3,  8,  5,  2,  6
```

a Copy the table below and use the above data to complete it.

Days of absence	Tally	Frequency
Fewer than 5	ɭɬɬ̄ ǀǀ	7
5		
6		
7		
8		
9		
10		
More than 10		

b Draw a bar chart, on graph paper, to represent the same data. Let 2 cm represent both one division on the horizontal axis and one unit of frequency on the vertical axis.
c Work out the number of students in the class.
d Find the fraction of the students who were absent 8 times.
e Find the fraction of the students who were absent 7 times.

Given that the whole school contains 800 students, and the above class is typical regarding absence, work out the number of students in the whole school who would be likely to be absent
f 8 times,
g 7 times.

6 A sample of 720 people are asked how they intend to vote at the General Election. The results are shown in the pie chart.

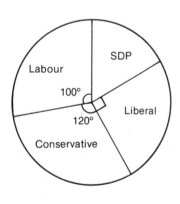

How many people intend to vote
a Conservative?
b Labour?
c Liberal?
d Liberal or SDP?

7 Work out the mode, median, mean and range of the following numbers:

12, 11, 10, 27, 15, 12, 11, 11, 17

8 The medals obtained by a certain country in four successive Olympic Games are shown in the following table.

	1972	1976	1980	1984
Gold	3	2	5	4
Silver	5	4	6	7
Bronze	8	9	10	5
Totals	16			

Work out
a the totals for 1976, 1980 and 1984,
b the total number of medals that the country wins in the four Games,
c the mean number of medals obtained per Games,
d the mean number of gold medals obtained per Games.

October

November

December

January

February

= 120 bottles

9 The pictogram shows the numbers of bottles of wine sold by an off-licence in a 5-month period. The numbers are rounded off to the nearest 120.

Work out
a the number of bottles sold (to the nearest 120) in each of the 5 months,
b the total for the 5-month period,
c the mean number of bottles sold per month,
d the range of the bottles sold per month.

10 The mean of 20, 25 and another number is 30. What is the other number?

11 The mean price of seven articles is £4.
a What is the total price of the articles?

The mean price of another three articles is £14.
b What is the total price of these articles?

Use your answers to **a** and **b** to work out
c the total price of all 10 articles.

Hence work out
d the mean price of the 10 articles.

12 A cricket team's scores in all the innings they have in a season are as follows:

156, 107, 305, 188, 327, 563, 203, 247, 264,
258, 319, 224, 87, 273, 238, 439, 259, 165,
219, 280, 372, 231, 335, 134, 321, 230, 260,
340, 236, 275, 126, 206, 194, 295, 173, 142

a Copy the table below and use the above data to complete it.

Score	Tally	Frequency
Fewer than 100		
100–150		
151–200		
201–250		
251–300		
301–350		
More than 350		

b Display the data in the form of a bar chart, using a scale of 2 cm to each division on the horizontal axis and a scale of 2 cm to one unit of frequency on the vertical axis.

c How many innings did the team have altogether?

d What fraction of their scores were between 201 and 250?

e What fraction of their scores were between 251 and 300?

f From the original data, work out the range of the scores.

13 An Italian restaurant offers a choice of pizza, lasagne, steak, spaghetti or veal for the main dish. One evening 120 people eat there, their choices being indicated in the pie chart.

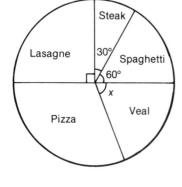

Work out the number that choose

a lasagne,

b spaghetti,

c steak.

Given that 24 people choose veal, work out

d the angle *x*,

e the number that choose pizza.

Further statistics

Exercise 24A

1 One evening a girl spends 40% of her time on homework, 25% watching television, 20% washing her hair and 15% listening to records. Display this information in a pie chart, stating the angles at the centre.

2 A street contains five families with no children, six families with one child, eight families with two children and two families with three children. Find the mode, median and mean of the number of children per family.

3 The temperature at a certain place is recorded at 12 noon on a number of successive days. The results are shown in the following frequency table.

Temperature (°C)	7–9	9–11	11–13	13–15	15–17
Frequency	2	3	5	4	2

a Draw a histogram to represent this information, letting 1 cm stand for 1°C on the horizontal axis and letting 2 cm stand for 1 unit of frequency on the vertical axis.

b State the modal class.

c Work out the number of days on which the temperature was recorded.

d Work out the fraction of the days on which the temperature was between 13°C and 17°C.

4 Find the mode, median and mean of the following sets of numbers:
a 5, −2, −1, 1, −2, −1, 0, −1, 2, 9, 1, 7
b 25, 41, 20, 70, 41, 55, 25, 23, 41, 29

5 Each pupil in a class is asked how many sisters he or she has. The results are shown in the following frequency table.

Number of sisters	0	1	2	3
Frequency	10	8	5	2

Work out
a the modal number of sisters,
b the median number of sisters,
c the number of pupils in the class,
d the total number of sisters,
e the mean number of sisters per pupil.

6 Find the mode, median and mean of the sets of numbers indicated by the following frequency tables.

a

Number	0	1	2	3
Frequency	5	4	4	2

b

Number	−5	−3	−1	1	3
Frequency	4	5	2	7	2

7 A boy takes three maths tests and obtains a mean mark of 62%. What mark must he get at his next test to bring his mean mark up to 70%?

8 One summer the weather is recorded on 144 days. Of these, 32 are classed as sunny, 40 as dull, 44 as showery and 28 as wet. Draw a pie chart to represent this information, stating the angles at the centre.

9 The histogram on the left shows the results of measuring the weights of a set of objects.
a State the modal class.
b Work out the total number of objects weighed.
c Estimate the mean weight of an object by taking mid-interval values (e.g. assume that all the objects in the 10–20 interval have weights of 15 kg).

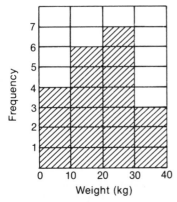

10 The following table records the number of goals scored by a hockey team in a series of matches.

Goals	Fewer than 2	2	3	4
Frequency	8	7	6	3

From this information it is possible to work out only **one** of the three averages (mean, median, mode). State which average can be found and give its value.

11 The lengths of a set of articles, in centimetres, are as follows:

16·6, 19·0, 15·6, 18·2, 16·7, 17·7, 19·1, 17·9, 17·6, 16·9,
18·4, 17·2, 16·2, 16·4, 16·6, 18·8, 20·2, 19·2, 17·0, 19·9,
17·6, 15·9, 17·3, 15·8, 17·4

a Copy the table below and use the above data to complete it.

Length (cm)	15·5–16·5	16·5–17·5	17·5–18·5	18·5–19·5	19·5–20·5
Frequency					

b From the table draw a histogram, using 2 cm for 1 unit on each axis.
c State the modal class.
d Work out the fraction of the articles that have lengths between 17·5 cm and 19·5 cm.
e Estimate the mean length, using mid-interval values.

12 The ages of 12 children at a party are as shown in the following frequency table.

Age	8	9	10	11
Frequency	2	3	6	1

Work out
a the mode of the ages,
b the median age,
c the mean age.

A man and his wife, who are of the same age, are in charge of the party. If the ages of these two adults are taken into account, the average age of all the people is 13. Work out
d the total age of all the fourteen people,
e the total age of the two adults,
f the actual age of each of the adults.

Exercise 24B

1 At a New Year's Eve party 10% of the guests chose non-alcoholic drinks, 30% drank beer and 60% drank wine. Display this information in a pie chart, stating the angles at the centre.

2 At the supermarket, a man buys four articles costing 50p each, two costing £1.10 each, three costing £2.40 each and one costing £3.20. Work out the mode, median and mean values of the price he pays for an article.

3 The heights of a group of people are measured, with the results shown in the following frequency table.

Height (inches)	60–63	63–66	66–69	69–72	72–75	75–78
Frequency	3	7	12	10	6	2

a Display this information in a histogram, letting 2 cm represent each 3 cm division on the horizontal axis, and letting 1 cm represent 1 unit of frequency on the vertical axis.

b State the modal class.

c Work out the number of people whose heights were measured.

d Work out the percentage of the people whose heights were between 66 inches and 75 inches.

4 Find the range, mode, median and mean of the following sets of numbers:

a 2, 2, 3, 3, 3, 3, 4, 4, 4, 4, 6, 9,

b 7, −8, −3, 7, −10, 4, −8, 5, 7, −3,

c 200, 100, 150, 150, 300, 200, 250, 150.

5 A survey is carried out to find out how many bedrooms the houses in Sandhill Road have. The results are shown in the following frequency table.

Number of bedrooms	2	3	4	5	6
Frequency	4	20	14	7	5

Work out

a the modal number of bedrooms,

b the median number of bedrooms,

c the number of houses in the road,

d the total number of bedrooms,

e the mean number of bedrooms per house (as a decimal).

6 One day the times allotted to a student's classes are as shown in the following table.

Subject	Maths	Physics	Chemistry	General Studies
Time (minutes)	80	90	30	40

Display this information in the form of a pie chart, stating the angles at the centre.

7 Find the mode, median and mean of the sets of numbers indicated by the following frequency tables.

a

Number	−4	−3	−2	−1	0	1	2
Frequency	9	6	3	3	2	1	1

b

Number	10	15	20	25	30
Frequency	7	8	3	5	7

8 The mean weight of five articles is 40 g. A sixth article is added, and the mean drops to 38 g. What is the weight of this article?

9 The distribution of ages of the children in a small school is shown in the following histogram.

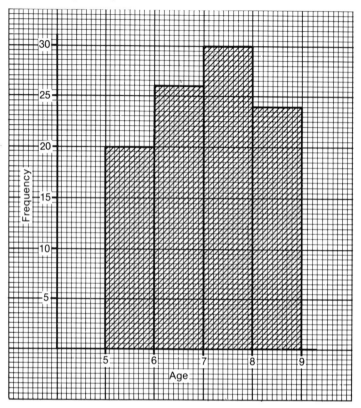

a State the modal class.
b Work out the number of children in the school.
c Estimate the mean age of the children, to one decimal place, by taking mid-interval values.

10 From the following table, showing the goals scored by a netball team in a series of matches, it is possible to find just two of the three averages.

Goals	Fewer than 3	3	4	5	More than 5
Frequency	8	12	10	7	4

State the averages that can be found, and give their values.

11 The weights of a set of articles, in kilograms, are as follows:

10·4, 11·1, 9·9, 8·7, 10·8, 9·8, 10·1, 10·6, 8·6, 10·2,
11·3, 9·1, 10·3, 9·7, 12·1, 9·4, 11·0, 10·0, 11·8, 11·4

a Copy the table below and use the above data to complete it.

Weight (kg)	8·5–9·5	9·5–10·5	10·5–11·5	11·5–12·5
Frequency				

b Draw a histogram of the data, letting 2 cm represent 1 unit on each axis.

c Work out the percentage of the articles whose weight is less than 10·5 kg.

d Estimate the mean weight of an article, using mid-interval values.

12 A cricketer has a mean score of 25 in his first two innings, and a mean score of 35 in his next two. In his fifth innings he scores 70. Work out his mean score for the five innings.

Probability

One-event probability

Note: *In this section give all probabilities as fractions in their lowest terms.*

1 The four cards shown are placed face down and shuffled, then one card is chosen at random. Find the probability that the card is
  a the king of spades,
  b an ace,
  c not the diamond.

2 A £1 coin is tossed repeatedly. Write down the probability that
  a the fifth toss gives a tail,
  b the fifth toss gives the same result as the fourth toss.

3 Joanne is offered a plate on which there are two jam doughnuts, four apple doughnuts and four Danish pastries. She can choose any one item.
  a If Joanne chooses in a completely random way, what is the probability that she gets a jam doughnut?
  b If Joanne decides that she will have a doughnut and not a pastry, but chooses among the doughnuts at random, what is the probability that she gets an apple doughnut?

4 When a biased coin is tossed the probability that it gives a head is $\frac{3}{5}$. What is the probability that it gives a tail?

5

The bottle shown contains 28 black marbles and 72 white ones. It is shaken, then one marble is taken out of it at random. What is the probability that the marble is black?

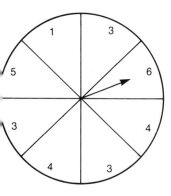

6 A fair dice is tossed once. Find the probability that it gives
  a a 4,
  b an even number,
  c a 5 or a 6.

7 The diagram on the left shows a fairground spinner. When the pointer is spun, find the probability that it lands on
  a a 5,
  b a 3,
  c a 4,
  d a number greater than 3.

8 A whole number is chosen at random from the numbers between 95 and 109 inclusive. What is the probability that the number has two digits?

9 In the quarter-final of the FA Cup competition, Arsenal, Manchester United, Manchester City and five other teams are left. When the draw is made for the quarter-final, find the probability that
  a Arsenal is drawn to play Manchester United,
  b Arsenal is **not** drawn to play a Manchester club,
  c the two Manchester clubs are **not** drawn to play each other.

10 In a charity raffle with one prize, 150 tickets are sold. Given that Louise buys six tickets and Neela buys four, find the probability that
  a Louise gets the winning ticket,
  b one of the two girls gets the winning ticket,
  c Neela does not get the winning ticket.

11 Twenty children take a test and each is given a mark out of 10. The results are shown in the following table.

Mark	0–2	3	4	5	6	7	8–10
Number of children	1	2	3	4	4	3	3

If one of the children is chosen at random, find the probability that he or she gets
  a 6 marks,
  b at least 6 marks,
  c more than 2 marks but less than 5.

12 All the staff of a printing firm are asked their favourite sport. The results are shown in the bar chart on the left.

If one of the staff is chosen at random, find the probability that their favourite sport is
  a snooker,
  b cricket,
  c cricket or football,
  d not tennis.

13 One ball is chosen at random from a box of balls. The probability that it is one of the four red balls in the box is $\frac{2}{11}$. How many balls does the bag contain altogether?

14 Roxanne is equally likely to receive £1 or £2 pocket money and Judy is equally likely to be given £1, £2 or £3. Copy and complete the following table, in which all the possible sums of their pocket moneys are to be shown.

Roxanne	Judy	Total
£1	£1	£2
£1	£2	£3

a What is the probability that the total is exactly £4?
b One week the two girls want to club together and buy a pair of earrings which costs £3.70. What is the probability that they receive enough pocket money to do this?

15 A 2p coin, a 5p coin and a 10p coin are tossed together. Copy and complete the table below, showing all the possible outcomes ('H' stands for 'heads' and 'T' stands for 'tails').

2p coin	5p coin	10p coin
H	H	H
H	H	T
H	T	H

a How many possible outcomes are there altogether?
b What is the probability that exactly two heads are obtained?
c What is the probability that all the three coins give the same result?

Exercise 25B

1 A bag of fruit flavoured sweets contains three lemon flavour, two blackcurrant flavour and one strawberry flavour. One sweet is taken from the bag at random. Find the probability that it is
a lemon flavour,
b blackcurrant flavour,
c lemon or strawberry flavour,
d not strawberry flavour.

2 It is estimated that a horse's chance of winning a race is $\frac{2}{7}$. On this basis, what is the probability that the horse will not win the race?

3 A teacher has to choose one child from James, Anita, Julie, Pablo, Tom and Alec. If she chooses from all the children at random, find the probability that she selects

a a boy,
b Julie,
c James or Anita.

If, on the other hand, the teacher decides that it is essential to have a boy, but she chooses from all the boys at random, find the probability that
d she selects Pablo,
e she does not select Alec.

4 One letter is chosen at random from the word NINETYNINE. Find the probability that it is
a the Y,
b an E,
c an N.

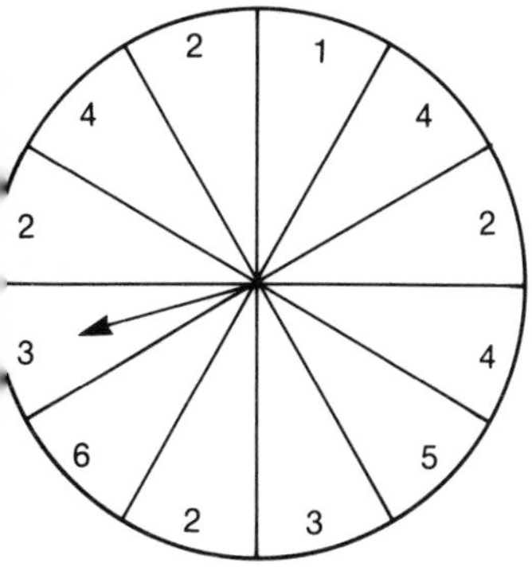

5 When the pointer on the left is spun, find the probability that it lands on
a a 5,
b a 2,
c a 2 or a 3 or a 4.

6 A firm employs 42 men and 18 women. If one employee is selected at random, what is the probability that it will be a man?

7 The tally chart below shows the items on one of the tables at a party.

	Tally
Hot-dogs	||||
Sandwiches	卌 |||
Cakes	卌
Biscuits	卌 ||

If one of these items is chosen at random, find the probability that it is
a a sandwich,
b a hot-dog,
c a cake or a biscuit.

8 An ordinary pack of cards (containing 52 cards) is shuffled, and then cards are dealt from it one-by-one. Given that the first two cards dealt are aces, find the probability that the next card is
a another ace,
b a king.

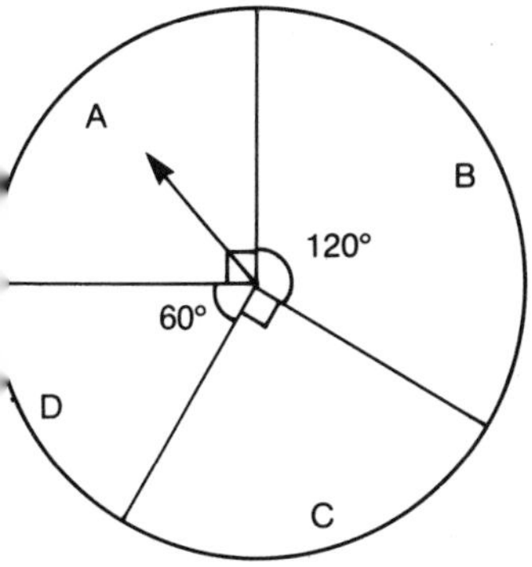

9 Five children are arranged in a line at random, including Jacob and his sister. Find the probability that Jacob stands next to his sister, given that
a Jacob is at one of the end positions,
b Jacob is not at one of the end positions.

10 When the pointer on the left is spun, find the probability that it lands in
a region A,
b region B,
c region D,
d region C or region D.

11 One number is chosen at random from all the whole numbers between 11 and 30 inclusive. Find the probability that the number is
  a even,
  b a perfect square,
  c a prime number,
  d over 14.

12 The bar chart on the left shows the contents of Michelle's money box. If one coin is taken from the box at random, find the probability that it is
  a a 20p coin,
  b a 2p coin,
  c a 2p coin or a 10p coin:

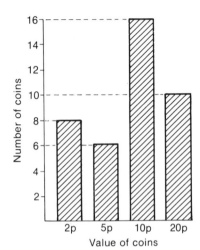

13 In a group of people there are six who have ginger hair. When one person is selected from the group at random, the probability that he or she has ginger hair is $\frac{2}{9}$. How many people are there in the group?

14 Alvin and Carol are each asked to choose one of the numbers 3, 4 or 5, and then the two numbers chosen are added together. Copy and complete the table below, to show all the possible results.

		CAROL		
		3	4	5
A	3	6	7	
L	4			
V	5			
I				
N				

Find the probability that the sum of the two numbers is
  a 7,
  b 8,
  c more than 7,
  d an even number.

15 When a boy goes ice-skating he can either travel to the ice rink by bus, which takes 40 minutes, or by train, which takes 25 minutes. One day he goes ice-skating and comes home again, in each case choosing his means of transport by tossing a coin. Make a table to show the total time he spends in travelling for all the different ways he can make his two journeys. Use the table to find the probability that
  a he spends 50 minutes travelling altogether,
  b he spends 65 minutes travelling altogether,
  c he spends longer coming home than going.

Simple combined probabilities

Exercise 26A

1 When Simon fires a shot at a target his probability of a hit is $\frac{2}{5}$, and when Mandy fires her probability of a hit is $\frac{5}{8}$.

If Simon fires twice, find the probability that he gets
a two hits,
b two misses.

If they both fire one shot, find the probability that
c Simon misses and Mandy hits,
d they both miss.

2 An ordinary (fair) dice is tossed once, and a coin is tossed twice. Find the probability of
a a 6 and two heads,
b a number below 3 and two tails.

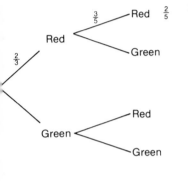

3 Two balls are drawn at random, without replacement, from a box containing four red balls and two green balls. Copy and complete the tree diagram on the left showing all the possible outcomes and their probabilities. (The fraction on the right is the product of the fractions on the two branches.)

Use the tree diagram to find the probability that
a two balls of the same colour are drawn,
b at least one green ball is drawn.

4 A coin which is known to be biased is thrown 2500 times and gives a head 1487 times.
a Estimate, to one decimal place, the probability that the coin gives a head on any single throw.

The coin is thrown three times. On the basis of the above estimate, work out, as a decimal, the probability that the sequence of results is
b head, tail, head,
c tail, head, tail.

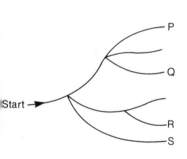

5 The diagram on the left represents a network of roads. A man goes for a walk, starting as shown. When he comes to a junction the probability that he takes the left fork is $\frac{2}{3}$, and if he does not take the left fork he is equally likely to take any of the other roads available. He never retraces his steps. Find the probability that he eventually reaches
a the point P,   c the pont R,
b the point Q,   d the point S.

6 Assuming that any baby born is equally likely to be a boy or a girl, find the probability that a family of four children are all boys. Deduce the probability that a family of four children contains at least one girl.

7 I drive to work, on average, on three days out of every five and I go by bus on the other days. When I drive, my probability of getting to work on time is $\frac{2}{3}$, and when I go by bus it is $\frac{5}{7}$. Find the probability that, on any particular day,
a I go to work by bus,
b I drive and am late for work,
c I go by bus and arrive on time.

8 Find the probability that
a two people chosen at random
b three people chosen at random
were born on different days of the week.

9 Patrick and Mohammed play a game with a dice. Patrick throws first and wins the game if he gets a 5 or a 6. Otherwise Mohammed throws and wins the game if he gets a 4, 5 or 6. If neither boy wins they play the game again, with Mohammed throwing first. Find the probability that

a Patrick wins the first game,
b Mohammed wins the first game,
c neither boy wins the first game, then Mohammed wins the second.

Is the game fair? Explain your answer, briefly.

10 When Tom plays Pippa at chess he wins, on average, half of the games and Pippa wins one game in six. The rest of the games are draws. One afternoon they play two games. Draw a tree diagram to show all the possible outcomes and their probabilities, and find the probability that

a the same result occurs in both games,
b at least one draw occurs,
c Tom and Pippa both win one game.

11 My probability of beating a certain opponent at darts is x. If we play two games, what is my probability of losing them both?

12 In Paris, at a certain time of the year, the probability that it rains on any given day is $\frac{1}{3}$. Find the probability that, on three successive days,

a it does not rain at all,
b it rains at least once.

13 Five equally matched children, Jason, Sue, Akbar, Judy and Moira, run a race. Find the probability that

a Jason wins,
b Judy is third,
c Sue wins and Akbar is second,
d Moira wins and Jason is not last.

14 One box contains ten cards marked '1' and twenty cards marked '2', while another box contains ten cards marked '1' and five cards marked '2'. One card is taken at random from each box and the numbers on them are added together. Copy and complete the tree diagram below, showing the possible outcomes and their probabilities. Use the tree diagram to find the probability that the total is

a 3,
b at least 3.

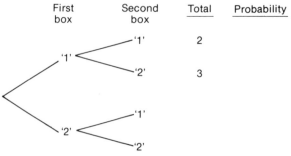

15 Yorkshire, Hampshire, Surrey and Somerset reach the semi-final of a cricket knockout competiton. Assuming that the teams are equally

likely to win any particular game, and the draw for the semi-final is random, find the probability that
a Yorkshire beat Surrey in the semi-final, then lose the final,
b Somerset reach the final,
c Hampshire beat Surrey in the final.

Exercise 26B

1 Charles and Katia are both about to take their driving test. If Charles's probability of passing is $\frac{3}{4}$ and Katia's is $\frac{2}{3}$, find the probability that
a they both pass,
b Charles passes and Katia fails,
c they both fail.

2 Three of the horses in a race have winning probabilities of $\frac{1}{4}$, $\frac{1}{6}$ and $\frac{1}{8}$, respectively. Find the probability that
a one of the three horses wins,
b none of the horses win.

3 My pocket contains three 2p coins and two 5p coins. I draw out two coins at random, without replacement. Draw a tree diagram to show all the possibilities and use it to find the probability that I draw
a a total of 7p,
b two coins of the same kind.

4 Each of two people selects, at random, one of the whole numbers from 5 to 9 inclusive. Find the probability that
a each person selects an odd number,
b each person selects a prime number.

5 A biased dice is thrown 3000 times and gives a six 870 times.
a Estimate the probability, to one decimal place, that the dice gives a 6 on any single throw.
b On the basis of this estimate, work out the probability that when the dice is thrown three times it gives a 6 followed by a non-6 followed by a 6.

6 When Alison plays her friend at chess, her probability of winning any particular game is $\frac{1}{4}$. One evening they play three games. Find the probability that
a Alison loses all three games,
b Alison wins one or more of the games.
(Assume that draws never occur.)

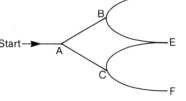

7 The diagram on the left represents a network of roads. A car starts as shown and never retraces its path. When it comes to a junction the probability that it takes the left fork is 0·7. Giving each answer as a decimal, find the probability that the car reaches
a the point D,
b the point F,
c the point E via B,
d the point E via C.

From your answers to c and d, deduce
e the car's overall probability of reaching the point E.

8   The aces and kings are taken from a pack, and then from these eight cards two cards are selected at random. Find the probability that
a the first card is an ace and the second is a king,
b both cards are kings,
c the first card is a heart and the second is a spade.

9   The probability that a certain man will get married is $\frac{2}{3}$, and if he gets married the probability that he will buy a house is $\frac{3}{4}$. If he does not get married the probability that he will buy a house is $\frac{1}{4}$. Find the probability that
a the man marries and does not buy a house,
b he does not marry and buys a house.

10 A box initially contains three red balls and one black ball. When a red ball is taken from the box it is not replaced, but when a black ball is taken it is replaced by two black balls. Draw a tree diagram to show the possible results of two successive random selections, and find the probability that
a the second ball is red,
b two balls of different colours are drawn.

11 The probability that a woman watches television on any particular day is x. Write down an expression for the probability that she watches television on Monday and Tuesday but does not watch on Wednesday.

12 Fiona, Robert, Winston and Charlotte are waiting to be interviewed for a job. If the order in which they are interviewed is decided in a random way, find the probability that
a Robert is interviewed last,
b Fiona is first and Winston is second,
c the women are the first two to be interviewed.

13 Two girls play a game using just the aces, kings and queens from an ordinary pack of cards. One of the girls draws a card at random, and she wins the game if she gets a diamond. If she fails, the card is replaced, the second girl draws, and she wins if she gets an ace. If neither girl wins the game is repeated. Work out whether the game is fair, explaining your answer.

14 I always go to work by bus or by train. When I go by bus the probability that I change my method of transport on the following day is $\frac{2}{3}$, and when I go by train the probability that I change is $\frac{1}{4}$. Given that I go by bus on Tuesday, draw a tree diagram to show all my possible methods of transport for Wednesday and Thursday, and use the diagram to find the probability that
a I go by train on Thursday,
b I go by bus on exactly one of the two days,
c I use the same method of transport on Wednesday and Thursday.

Algebra

Substitution of values into algebraic expressions

Quick revision exercise 27

1　Work out the value of
   a　$P + Q$ when $P = 7$ and $Q = 10$,
   b　$2T + 3S$ when $T = 5$ and $S = 6$,
   c　$7x - 4y$ when $x = 5$ and $y = 8$,
   d　$6m + n + 3p$ when $m = 2$, $n = 5$ and $p = 1$,
   e　$2P - Q - R$ when $P = 9$, $Q = 7$ and $R = 4$,
   f　$5w - 2r + 3t$ when $w = 10$, $r = 8$ and $t = 2$.

2　Work out the value of
   a　NW when $N = 11$ and $W = 5$,
   b　xyz when $x = 2$, $y = 6$ and $z = 3$,
   c　mps when $m = 5$, $p = 0$ and $s = 1$,
   d　$3(p + s)$ when $p = 7$ and $s = 2$,
   e　$T(R - T)$ when $T = 4$ and $R = 6$,
   f　$(v - u)(u + 4)$ when $v = 3$ and $u = 1$,
   g　$(2m + n)(m - 3n)$ when $m = 7$ and $n = 2$.

3　Work out the value of

   a　$\dfrac{10L}{R}$ when $L = 6$ and $R = 5$,

   b　$\dfrac{x + y}{2y}$ when $x = 3$ and $y = 9$,

   c　$\dfrac{5M + T}{M}$ when $M = 3$ and $T = 6$,

   d　$\dfrac{2r}{r - s}$ when $r = 12$ and $s = 4$,

   e　$\dfrac{P + Q}{P - Q}$ when $P = 45$ and $Q = 30$,

   f　$\dfrac{2(x + 2w)}{3x}$ when $x = 2$ and $w = 8$,

4　Work out the value of
   a　x^2 when $x = 4$,
   b　y^2 when $y = 11$,
   c　$2r^2$ when $r = 3$
   d　mp^2 when $m = 4$ and $p = 5$,
   e　$(sv)^2$ when $s = 6$ and $v = 2$,
   f　$T^2 - W^2$ when $T = 3$ and $W = 1$,
   g　$(H - F)^2$ when $H = 9$ and $F = 2$,
   h　$2P^2 - 3R^2$ when $P = 4$ and $R = 2$.

Algebraic formulae

1 A group of friends go on a trip to Southend and share the cost equally. The total cost of the trip is then given by the formula

    total cost = cost per person × number of people

Use this formula to find the total cost when
a the cost per person is £5.50 and 20 people go on the trip,
b 32 people go and each person pays £4.20.

2 a If a car has 10 litres in its tank and travels 8 miles to the litre, how many miles can it travel before running out of petrol?
b Use the reasoning of part **a** to find a formula for D, where D miles is the distance that can be travelled by a car that does m miles to the litre and has N litres in its tank.

3 The diagram shows two angles on a straight line. When the value of x is known y can be found by the formula

$$y = 180 - x$$

Use this formula to find y when
a $x = 25$,
b $x = 143$.

4 The time, T minutes, that it takes to cook a chicken of weight w pounds is given by the formula

$$T = 20w + 15$$

a Find T when $w = 3\frac{1}{2}$.
b Find the time it takes to cook a $4\frac{1}{4}$ lb chicken.

5 The diagram represents a three-sided fence which is built against a wall to form a rectangular garden.

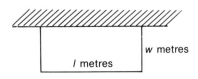

a Write down a formula for P, where P metres is the total length of the fencing.
b Find P when $l = 20$ and $w = 12$.
c Find P when $l = 18.5$ and $w = 13.25$.
d Write down a formula for A, where A m^2 is the area of the garden.
e Find A when $l = 28$ and $w = 16.5$.

6 A man buys n digital watches for £x each and sells them for a total price of £y.
a Write down a formula for the man's profit, £p, in terms of n, x and y.
b Find p when $n = 6$, $x = 8$ and $y = 60$.
c Find the profit when 10 articles are bought for £3 each and sold for a total of £34.
d Find p when $n = 15$, $x = 4.2$ and $y = 71$.

7 A Local Authority is planning some road work. It knows from past experience that when N men work on L miles of road, the time taken, T days, is approximately given by the formula

$$T = \frac{20L}{N}$$

On the basis of this formula, work out
a how long 6 men will take to do 3 miles of the road work,
b how long 12 men will take to do $4\frac{1}{2}$ miles of the road work.

8   A salesperson is paid according to the formula

$$£P = £400x + £25y$$

where $£P$ is her pay for working for x months and selling y articles.
a How much does the salesperson earn in 3 months if she sells 24 articles in that time?
b How much would she be paid if she worked for a month without managing to sell any articles at all?

The salesperson's pay can be regarded as a basic salary plus a commission for each article she sells. Work out
c the basic salary for a month,
d the basic salary for a year,
e the commission paid on each article sold.

9   When a stone is dropped, the distance, d metres, that it falls in t seconds is given by the formula

$$d = 5t^2$$

Work out the distance the stone drops in
a 2 seconds, b 0.5 seconds, c 3.2 seconds.

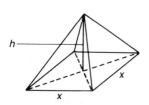

10 a Write down a formula for the perimeter, p cm, of the figure on the left.
b Find p when $x = 15$.
c Find the perimeter of the figure when its height is 5 cm.
d Write down a formula for the area, A cm², of the figure.
e Find A when $x = 6$.
f Find the area of the figure when its perimeter is 32 cm.

11 It can be shown that the number of diagonals that can be drawn in a polygon with n sides is given by the formula

$$N = \frac{n}{2}(n - 3)$$

a Use the formula to find the number of diagonals that can be drawn in a pentagon (5-sided polygon), and check your answer with a sketch.
b Find the number of diagonals that can be drawn in a 10-sided polygon.
c Find the number of diagonals that can be drawn in a 25-sided polygon.

12 The diagram shows a pyramid on a square base. The formula for its volume is
$$V = \frac{x^2h}{3}$$
Find the volume of
a a pyramid in which $x = 6$ cm and h = 10 cm,
b five pyramids of height 9 cm whose bases are squares of area 16 cm².

13 An assembler of portable radios is paid a basic £16 per day. As an incentive, if he assembles more than 50 radios in a day he is paid a bonus of £2 for each extra radio.

  a Work out how much he is paid for a day in which he assembles 62 radios.

  b Given that the man earns £W in a day for assembling N radios, where N is greater than 50, use the reasoning of part **a** to obtain a formula for W in terms of N.

Exercise 28B

1 A cricketer's average score is given by the formula

$$\text{average} = \frac{\text{runs scored}}{\text{number of innings}}$$

Find the average score of a cricketer who
  a scores 230 runs in 5 innings,
  b scores 546 runs in 14 innings.

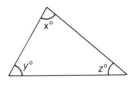

2 When two of the angles of the triangle on the left are given, the third angle can be found by the formula

$$z = 180 - x - y$$

Find z when
  a $x = 70$ and $y = 50$,
  b $x = 36$ and $y = 117$.

3 A woman buys x articles costing 5p each and y articles costing 8p each.
  a Write down a formula for t, where t pence is the total amount she spends.
  b Find t when $x = 6$ and $y = 3$.
  c Find t when $x = 17$ and $y = 21$.

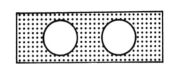

4 From a rectangular piece of cardboard of area A cm², two circles, each of area x cm², are cut out.
  a Write down a formula for R, where R cm² is the area of the remaining cardboard.
  b Find R when $A = 30$ and $x = 7$.
  c Find the area remaining when $A = 91$ and $x = 24$.

5 The formula for converting degrees Fahrenheit to degrees Centigrade is

$$C = \frac{5}{9}(F - 32)$$

Use this formula to convert to degrees Centigrade
  a 50°F,
  b 77°F,
  c 23°F,
  d 46°F, to one decimal place.

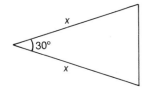

6 The area of the isosceles triangle shown is given by the formula

$$A = \frac{1}{4}\, x^2$$

Find the area of the triangle when
a $x = 8$ cm,
b $x = 11$ m.

7 The cost, £C, of hiring a car and driving it m miles, is given by the formula

$$C = 20 + \frac{m}{5}$$

Work out how much it costs to hire a car and drive it
a 40 miles,
b 170 miles,
c 83 miles

The total charge for hiring a car can be considered to consist of a standing charge together with a charge of a certain amount per mile.
Work out
d the standing charge,
e the charge per mile, in pence.

8 A body accelerates at a fixed rate from a speed of u m/s to a speed of v m/s. If the time this takes is t seconds, the distance travelled by the body, x metres, is given by the formula

$$x = \left(\frac{u + v}{2}\right) t$$

a Find x when $u = 7$, $v = 22$ and $t = 6$.
b Find the distance travelled by a body which takes 11 seconds to accelerate at a fixed rate from rest to a speed of 24 m/s.

9 The sum of the first n whole numbers is given by the formula

$$S = \frac{n}{2}\,(n + 1)$$

a Use the formula to find the sum of the first six whole numbers and check your answer by adding up the numbers.
b Find the sum of the numbers on a clock face.
c Find the sum of the whole numbers from 1 to 55 inclusive.
d By finding S when $n = 9$ and S when $n = 30$, find the sum of the whole numbers from 10 to 30 inclusive.

10 In a block of flats there are x flats with two bedrooms and y flats with three bedrooms. Write down expressions for
a the total number of flats,
b the total number of bedrooms.
Hence write down
c an expression for the average number of bedrooms per flat.

Use your answer to part **c** to find the average number of bedrooms per flat when
d $x = 15$ and $y = 5$,
e $x = 22$ and $y = 28$.

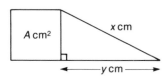

11 The area, A cm², of the square shown in the diagram is given by the formula

$$A = x^2 - y^2$$

Find A when
a $x = 6$ and $y = 4$,
b $x = 11$ and $y = 7$,
c $x = 23.5$ and $y = 14.5$.

12 Before a boy takes an examination his father offers to give him 10p per mark for every mark he gets up to and including 50, and 20p per mark for every mark over 50. Write down a formula for the amount of money, M pence, that he receives if
a he gets x marks and x is 50 or less,
b he gets y marks and y is over 50.

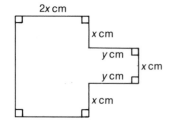

13 **a** Write down a formula for P, where P cm is the perimeter of the figure on the left.
b Find the perimeter when $x = 3\frac{1}{2}$ and $y = 4\frac{1}{2}$.
c Write down a formula for A, where A cm² is the area of the figure.
d Find A when $x = 5$ and $y = 6$.

Note: *All the remaining algebra is Level 2.*

Basic algebraic techniques

Exercise 29A

Simplify the following expressions by adding and/or subtracting like terms:

1 $8 - 2x + 5x - 10$

2 $5x - y + 3x - 2y$

3 $a - 2b + 7b - 4a$

4 $-2x + w - 3p - w - p + 6x$

5 $7a - 6 - 2b - 3 + 5b - a$

6 $12t - 5s - t + 7q - 7t + 3s - 9q$

7 $4x^2 + 3x - 9x^2 - x$

8 $ab - 2c - 4ab - 3c$

9 $3xy - x - 2y + 4xy + 3x + y$

10 $5pq - p^2 + 3p - p^2 - 4p - 4pq$

Remove the brackets:

11	$2(5x + 3)$		**16**	$5w(3x - 7t)$
12	$4(x + 2y)$		**17**	$x(x + 2y)$
13	$-3(5a - 3b)$		**18**	$-3x(4x - 5y)$
14	$x(2 - y)$		**19**	$xy(2y + x - 1)$
15	$-2p(3s + 5)$		**20**	$5p(2p - 4 + 6pq)$

Factorise the following expressions:

21	$3x + 6$		**27**	$10a - 15ab + 20ac$
22	$8a + 12b$		**28**	$x^2 + 4x$
23	$15 + 20p - 25q$		**29**	$3y^2 + 18xy$
24	$7 - 14t - 35r$		**30**	$8xy - 6y^2 - 10yw$
25	$4x + xy$		**31**	$9abc + 21ab - 15a^2b$
26	$ab - 2ac + a$		**32**	$5x^2y - 15x^2y^2 + 20x^2yz$

Solve the following equations:

33	$2x + 5 = 13$		**44**	$\dfrac{x}{2} = 3$
34	$3x - 1 = 8$			
35	$7 - y = 2$		**45**	$\dfrac{w}{3} - 1 = 4$
36	$9 - 2y = 6$			
37	$11x + 2 = 7x + 6$		**46**	$\dfrac{y + 5}{2} = 6$
38	$8p - 1 = 5p + 3$			
39	$7 - 2x = 14 - x$		**47**	$\dfrac{4 - 2y}{3} = 2$
40	$3 - t = t + 8$			
41	$2(3x - 1) = 12$		**48**	$5 - \dfrac{3x}{2} = 7$
42	$3(2 - y) = 6$		**49**	$2\frac{1}{2}t = 3$
43	$4(r - 2) = 8(2r + 3)$		**50**	$1 - 2x = \dfrac{3 + x}{2}$

Exercise 29B

Simplify the following expressions by adding and/or subtracting like terms:

1	$7a + 4 - 2a - 5$		**5**	$3ab - 2a - 4b + 7a - ab - 2ab$
2	$9x - 10y - 3y - 2x$		**6**	$p^2 - p - 3p^2 + 4p$
3	$-p + 2q - 5r + 2p + 5r$		**7**	$-4xy + 5x^2 + 7y - xy + 2x^2 - 7x^2$
4	$4 - 2t + 12r - 3t - 7 - 9r$		**8**	$ax - 3xy + 2xa - ay + 2yx$

Remove the brackets:

9 $3(2x + 5)$

10 $-7(x - 3y)$

11 $6(8a + 5b)$

12 $p(4 - q)$

13 $2y(9x - 3w)$

14 $-4t(5t + 2r)$

15 $ab(4b - 2a - 3)$

Remove the brackets and simplify:

16 $5x + 3(2y - 4x)$

17 $2(4a - b) + a(3b - 5)$

18 $5(p - 2q) - 2(p + 3q)$

19 $x(2 + 3y) - 3y(x - 1)$

Factorise the following expressions:

20 $2x - 10$

21 $9p + 15q$

22 $12x - 18y + 24$

23 $4 - 16r - 20s$

24 $5x - 2xy$

25 $2ab - 4bc$

26 $14xy - 28yz + 35y^2$

27 $6ab - 12abc + 18a^2b$

28 $20x^2y - 15xy^2 + 5xy$

Solve the following equations:

29 $4x + 2 = 14$

30 $5x - 7 = 3$

31 $12 - 2y = 2$

32 $10 - 3x = -14$

33 $6x + 8 = 5x + 2$

34 $9p - 2 = 6p + 5$

35 $4 - t = t - 3$

36 $2(8x + 2) = 12$

37 $5(2 - 3y) = -20$

38 $2(p + 1) = 6(2 + p)$

39 $\dfrac{x}{5} = 2$

40 $\dfrac{3x}{4} = 9$

41 $\dfrac{y}{2} + 4 = 3$

42 $\dfrac{2z - 1}{2} = 3$

43 $6 - \dfrac{3w}{3} = 5$

44 $1\frac{1}{2}x = 5$

45 $2y - 5 = \dfrac{3y - 1}{3}$

Construction and solution of linear equations from given data

In these exercises all algebraic expressions should be put in the simplest possible form.

Exercise 30A

1 A hiker walks x km on Monday, $(x + 7)$ km on Tuesday and $(x - 3)$ km on Wednesday.
  a Write down an expression for the total distance she walks in the three days.

b Given that in fact she walks 88 km in the three days, form an equation and solve it to find x.

2 A woman buys an article for £($x + 10$) and sells it for £$3x$.
  a Write down an expression for the profit she makes.
  b Given that in fact she makes a profit of £6, form an equation, solve it, and hence find the prices the woman paid and received for the article.

3 Neville is x years old and his sister Carmel is 3 years younger.
  a Write expressions for the ages the children will be in 10 years' time.
  b Given that their total age in 10 years will be 35 years, form an equation, solve it, and hence find the children's present ages.

4 **a** Write down an expression for the cost of N postcards at 8p each and ($N + 2$) biros at 10p each.
  b Given that the postcards and biros cost £2 altogether, form an equation and solve it to find N.

5 Three angles have values of ($2p + 30$)°, ($p + 12$)° and ($p - 18$)°. Find the values of p and the three angles, given that
  a the first angle is 68° more than the second,
  b the three angles could form the angles of a triangle.

6 **a** Write down expressions for five consecutive even numbers, the smallest of which is n.
  b Given that the sum of five consecutive even numbers is 620, form an equation, solve it, and hence find the five numbers.

7 Mr Maxwell leaves £8700 in his will to be divided among his wife and two children, Paul and Eileen. Paul receives £x, Eileen get £100 more than Paul, and their mother gets twice as much as Eileen.
  a Write down expressions for the amounts that Eileen and Mrs Maxwell get.
  b Form an equation, solve it, and hence work out how much Mrs Maxwell gets.

8 The length and width of a rectangular field are ($2x - 10$)m and ($x + 30$) m, respectively.
  a Obtain an expression for the perimeter of the field.
  b Find the perimeter if $x = 50$.
  c Find x and the perimeter if the length of the field is 130 m.
  d Given that the perimeter is 550 m, find x and the width of the field.

9 A girl has y 2p coins, ($10 - y$) 5p coins and ($y + 3$) 10p coins.
  a Obtain an expression for the total amount of money she has.
  b Given that in fact she has £1.36, form an equation and solve it to find the value of y.

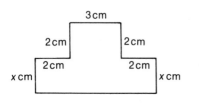

10 All the angles in the figure on the left are right angles.
  a Obtain expressions for the perimeter and the area of the figure.
  b Find x, given that the perimeter and the area are numerically equal.

11 **a** Write down a formula for the distance, x km, covered by a body which moves at a speed of v km/h for t hours.
  b A body travels at a speed of v km/h for 4 hours, then travels 5 km/h faster for 2 hours. Obtain an expression for the total distance it covers.
  c Given that in fact the total distance covered is 400 km, form an equation and solve it to find the value of v.

12 A job takes 40 hours altogether. One woman works at it for t hours, then another woman spends $(2t + 5)$ hours on it.

   a Obtain an expression for the time that remains to be spent on the job.

   b Given that a worker completes the third stage in 1 hour less than the first woman spent on the job, form an equation and solve it to find the value of t.

13 The rule for obtaining each term of the following sequence is '**double the last term and subtract 1**':

$$2, 3, 5, 9, 17, \ldots$$

   a Letting any term of the sequence be x, write down expressions for the next two terms.

   b Obtain an expression for the sum of x and the two terms which follow x.

   c Given that the sum obtained in **b** is 451, form an equation, solve it, and hence find the three terms.

diagram 1

$(2x - 15)°$

$x°$

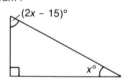

diagram 2

$3y°$ $2y°$

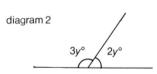

diagram 3 $(2p - 10)°$

$(p + 30)°$ $p°$

Exercise 30B

1 Joe earns £x per week, Salim earns twice as much as Joe, and Richard earns £20 less than Joe.

   a Write down expressions for the amounts that Salim and Richard earn.

   b If Salim earns £240, how much do Joe and Richard earn?

   c Given that Joe, Salim and Richard together earn a total of £340, form an equation, solve it, and hence find the amount that each man earns.

2 I need to study for 60 hours altogether in 3 weeks.

   a If I study for $3x$ hours in the first week and for $4x$ hours in the second, write down an expression for the number of hours I need to study in the third week.

   b Given that in fact I need to study for 11 hours in the third week, form an equation and solve it to find the value of x.

3 Three numbers can be expressed as y, $2y + 6$ and $4y + 20$. Find y, given that

   a the second number is 15 more than the first,

   b the second number and the third have a sum of 104,

   c the third number is 30 more than the second.

4 Find the values of x, y and p in diagrams 1 to 3.

5 **a** Write down an expression for the total cost of n articles at 12p each and $(n - 3)$ articles at 6p each.

   b Given that the total cost of these articles is £3.78, form an equation and solve it to find n.

6 The following is a simple sequence of numbers:

$$2, 5, 8, 11, 14, \ldots$$

a Letting any number in the sequence be x, write down expressions for the number just before this number and the two numbers just after it.

b Write down an expression for the sum of these four numbers.

c Given that the sum of the four numbers is 134, form an equation and solve it to find x.

7 A textbook contains p pages, a novel has 30 pages fewer than the textbook, and a dictionary has three times as many pages as the novel.

a Write down expressions for the numbers of pages that the novel and the dictionary have.

b Given that the total number of pages in the three books is 1230, form an equation, solve it, and hence find the number of pages in the dictionary.

8 Find x in the figure on the left given that

a the perimeter of the triangle is 68 cm,

b BC exceeds AB by 5 cm.

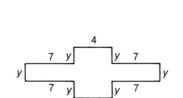

9 A man has $2y$ 10p coins and $(3y - 8)$ 20p coins. Find y, given that

a the man has the same amount of money in 10p coins and 20p coins,

b the total amount he has is £8.

10 In the figure on the left, all the angles are right angles and the distances shown are in centimetres. Find y if

a the perimeter is 45 cm,

b the perimeter is numerically equal to the area.

11 A train travels at 80 km/h for t hours, then at 100 km/h for $(t + 2)$ hours. Given that the total distance covered by the train is 470 km, find the value of t.

12 The rule for obtaining the terms of a certain type of sequence, given the first two terms, is '**add the two terms just before the term required**'. For example, a sequence of this type is

$$1, 3, 4, 7, 11, \ldots$$

a Given that the first two terms of such a sequence are 2, x, write down expressions for the third, fourth and fifth terms.

b Given that the sum of the first five terms of this sequence is 73, form an equation, solve it, and hence find the five terms.

Transformation of formulae

Exercise 31A

Make the letter given in brackets the subject of the formula:

1 $2x + y = 3$ (y) **2** $x - aw = t$ (x)

3 $p - r = 2$ (r)

4 $ax - y = 3 - w$ (y)

5 $wx = 7$ (w)

6 $2rs = 3$ (r)

7 $abc = d$ (c)

8 $ay + 4 = w$ (y)

9 $x + pw = 8$ (p)

10 $v = u + at = (t)$

11 $4x = m - 2r$ (r)

12 $a - 3y = 2 - 5at$ (t)

13 $5x - 3yw = w - 2p$ (y)

14 $x(2y - t) = 5$ (t)

15 $2v(v + 3ax) = y$ (x)

16 $\dfrac{x}{y} = 5$ (x)

17 $y = \dfrac{p}{2w}$ (p)

18 $\dfrac{t}{2x} = 3x$ (t)

19 $\dfrac{ax}{y} = 2$ (x)

20 $\dfrac{2pq}{5r} = 3t$ (p)

21 $m = 2 + \dfrac{r}{s}$ (r)

22 $x = \dfrac{2}{p}$ (p)

23 $\dfrac{a}{s} = \dfrac{w}{t}$ (s)

24 $4 = \dfrac{3}{2ax}$ (x)

25 $\dfrac{y}{a + x} = t$ (a)

26 $2p = \dfrac{w}{x + 3s}$ (s)

27 $s = (u + v)\dfrac{t}{2}$ (v)

28 $y = \dfrac{a}{p}(x - a)$ (x)

29 $\dfrac{2}{a + xy} = \dfrac{3}{t + x}$ (y)

30 $\dfrac{a + 2r}{x - y} = a$ (x)

Exercise 31B

Make the letter given in brackets the subject of the formula:

1 $x + 5w = 3$ (x)

2 $p - rs = y$ (p)

3 $2t = 7 - v$ (v)

4 $3m - y = 4 + x$ (y)

5 $6z = r$ (z)

6 $rt = wax$ (a)

7 $5pv^2 = 2m$ (p)

8 $ax + y = ws$ (x)

9 $4 - 3am = x$ (m)

10 $ab - c = 2 - aw$ (w)

11 $x^2y = pqr + q$ (r)

12 $x(y + 2w) = 3$ (w)

13 $3y(2 - ab) = s$ (a)

14 $4(a + 3) = x(a - y)$ (y)

15 $\dfrac{x}{2a} = 5$ (x)

16 $xy = \dfrac{m}{y}$ (m)

17 $\dfrac{2xy}{r} = \dfrac{t}{3}$ (y)

18 $\dfrac{ab}{cd} = \dfrac{cd}{b}$ (a)

19 $x + \dfrac{y}{r} = 3$ (y)

20 $5 = x - \dfrac{w}{2}$ (w)

21 $\dfrac{4}{y} = 3t$ (y)

22 $\dfrac{m}{v} = \dfrac{7}{m}$ (v)

23 $y = \dfrac{2}{5xw}$ (x)

24 $\dfrac{3ax}{2py} = \dfrac{p}{5x}$ (y)

25 $\dfrac{x}{r + s} = w$ (r)

26 $at = \dfrac{p}{a - c}$ (c)

27 $\dfrac{y}{2a} = \dfrac{3}{t + v}$ (t)

28 $\dfrac{a}{x}(r - 2) = 3$ (r)

29 $y = \dfrac{xy}{2}(ax - w)$ (w)

30 $\dfrac{2x}{x + y} = \dfrac{a}{p - t}$ (t)

Mensuration

1   Name the following figures fully (e.g. **isosceles triangle, right-angled isosceles triangle, rhombus, trapezium**, etc.)

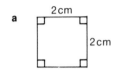
a

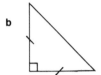
b

c

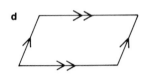
d

2   Find the perimeters of the following figures:
   a a triangle with sides of 7 cm, 9 cm, 11 cm;
   b a rectangle of length 18 cm and width 15 cm;
   c an isosceles triangle with equal sides of 6.5 m each and a third side of 4.5 m;
   d a quadrilateral with sides of 4.3 m, 5.6 m, 3.8 m, 7.2 m;
   e an equilateral triangle of side 12.6 cm.

3   Find the areas of the following figures:

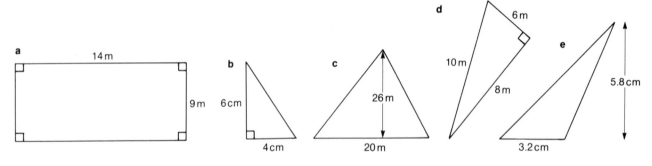

4   Find the perimeters and areas of the figures below. The rows of dots in parts **a** and **c** are 1 cm apart.

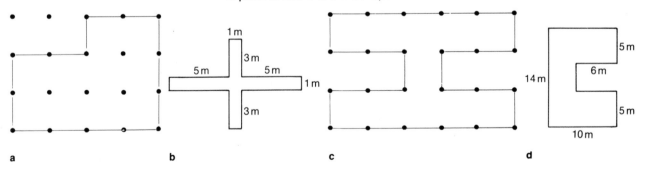

5   Find the volumes of the following figures;
   a a cube of side 3 cm;

b a cuboid (rectangular block) of length 5 cm, width 4 cm and height 2 cm;

c a cube of side 7 m;

d a cuboid of length 12 m, width $8\frac{1}{2}$ m and height $6\frac{1}{2}$ m.

6 By dividing the following figures into cuboids, find their volumes:

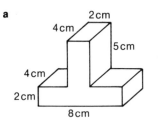
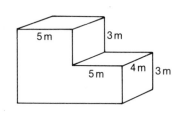

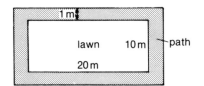

7 The diagram on the left shows a path of width 1 m around a rectangular lawn of length 20 m and width 10 m.
a Write down the length and width of the whole plot (lawn plus path).
Work out the area of
b the whole plot,
c the lawn,
d the path.

8 The diagram on the left shows an isosceles trapezium. Find the area of
a the central rectangle,
b one of the two right-angled triangles,
c the whole trapezium.

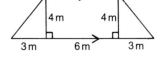

9 Find the areas of the figures below by dividing them into rectangles and triangles. The rows of dots are 1 cm apart.

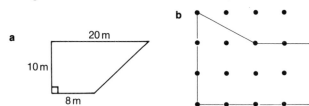

10 Taking π to be 3.14, work out the circumference of a circle with
a a diameter of 4 m,
b a radius of 6 m,
c a diameter of 10.5 cm.

11 The figures below are made up of semicircles and straight lines. Taking π to be 22/7, work out the perimeter of each figure.

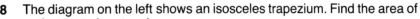
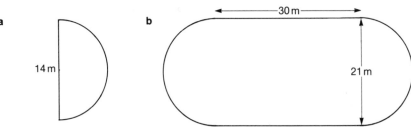

12 The figure below shows an open cardboard box, into which some boxes of matches, of the size indicated, are to be packed.

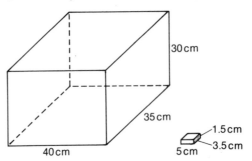

a How many boxes of matches will fit into the box?
b What area of cardboard is needed to make the box? (Remember that it has no top.)

13 The diagram on the left consists of six squares of side 2 cm and it represents the net of a cube. Work out
a the volume of the cube,
b its surface area.
Also draw
c two other nets of the same cube.

14 Each of the diagrams below represents the net of a cuboid. Work out the volume and the surface area of each cuboid.

a

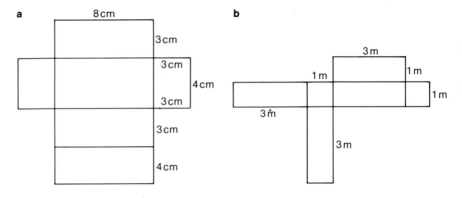

b

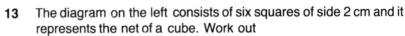

Exercise 32B

diagram 1

1 Name

a the figure shown in diagram 1;
b the figure shown in diagram 2;
c the figure formed on graph paper by the points (2, 0), (3, 1), (0, 3);
d the figure formed on graph paper by the points (1, −3), (4, −3), (4, −4), (2, −4).

(**Note:** *Use the same scale on both axes.*)

diagram 2

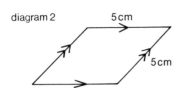

2 Find the perimeters of the following figures:
a an equilateral triangle of side 19 cm,

114

b a rectangle of length 4.5 cm and width 2.5 cm,
c an isosceles triangle with two sides of length 15 cm and a third side of half that length,
d a rhombus of side 13.7 m.

3 Find the areas of the following figures:

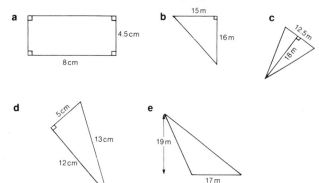

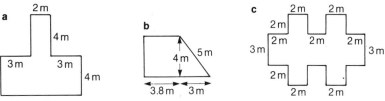

4 Find the perimeters and areas of the following figures:

5 Find the volumes of
a a cuboid of length and width 5 cm and height 4 cm,
b a cube of side 6 cm,
c a cuboid of length 18.2 cm, width 15 cm and height 4.5 cm.

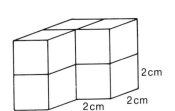

6 The figure on the left is made up of cubes of side 2 cm.
Work out:
a the volume of one of the cubes,
b the number of cubes in the figure,
c the volume of the figure.

If the figure is glued together and painted, work out
d how many of the square faces will be painted,
e the total area that will be painted.

7 Work out the number of faces, edges and corners each of the following figures has.

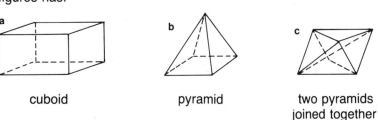

cuboid   pyramid   two pyramids
                                                       joined together

8 A rectangular lawn of length 36 m and width 30 m is surrounded by a path of width 2 m. Work out
  a the area of the whole plot,
  b the area of the lawn,
  c the area of the path.

9 Taking π to be 22/7, work out the circumference of a circle with
  a a diameter of 70 cm,
  b a radius of 42 cm.

10 The wheels of a model car each have a radius of 4 cm. Taking π to be 3.14, work out
  a the circumference of each wheel,
  b how far the car travels when the wheels rotate 50 times.

11 The rows of dots in this and later questions are 1 cm apart.

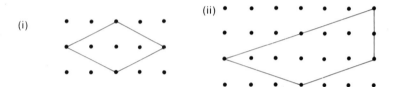

  a State the names of the two figures above.
  b By dividing the figure of diagram (i) into four right-angled triangles, work out its area.
  c By a similar method, work out the area of the figure in diagram (ii).

12 Say which of the following figures could represent the net of a cuboid:

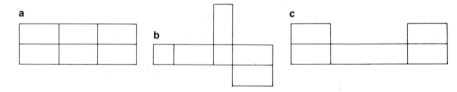

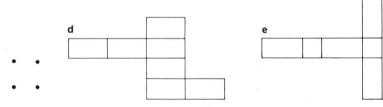

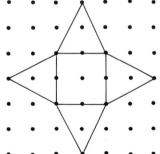

13 The figure on the left represents the net of a pyramid.

Work out
  a the area of the central square,
  b the area of one of the triangles,
  c the surface area of the pyramid.

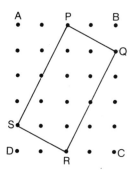

14 Work out the area of
a the rectangle ABCD,
b the triangle APS,
c the triangle PBQ.

Hence, by subtracting four triangles from the rectangle ABCD, work out:
d the area of the rectangle PQRS.

Further mensuration

Exercise 33A

1 Find the area of a circle with
a a radius of 5 m, taking π to be 3,
b a radius of 7 cm, taking π to be 22/7,
c a diameter of 40 cm, taking π to be 3.14,
d a diameter of 56 m, taking π to be 22/7.

2 Find the areas of the trapeziums below, using the formula
'average of parallel sides times distance between them'.

a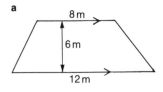

b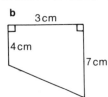

c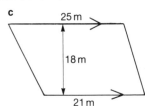

3 The diagram below represents a rectangular plot of land consisting of a lawn and two circular flower beds of radius 6 m.

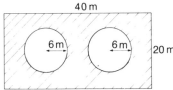

Taking π to be 3.14, work out, to the nearest whole number,
a the area of one of the flower beds,
b the area of the lawn (the shaded area).

4 The figure on the left shows the end view of a house of length 15 m.

Work out
a the area of the figure,
b the volume of the house.

5 Some iron cylinders, of radius 2 cm and length 6 cm, have to be made from a cubical block of iron of side 8 cm. Work out
 a the volume of the iron block,
 b the volume of one cylinder, taking π to be 3,
 c the number of cylinders that can be made from the block,
 d the volume of metal that is left over.

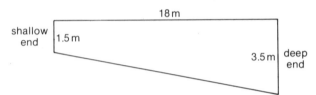

6 The diagram on the left shows a plot of land which consists of a rectangle and two semicircular ends. Work out the area of the plot, taking π to be 3.

7 A jar has a cross-sectional area of 80 cm² and contains water to a depth of 12 cm. Work out
 a the volume of water in the jar.

The water is poured into another jar of cross-sectional area 60 cm². Work out
 b the height of the water in the second jar.

8

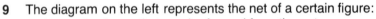

The diagram represents the cross-section of a swimming pool. Work out
 a the area of the cross-section.

Given that the pool is 12 m wide, work out
 b the volume of the pool.

9 The diagram on the left represents the net of a certain figure:
 a Name the figure that can be formed from the net.
 b Work out the volume of the figure.
 c Work out the surface area of the figure.

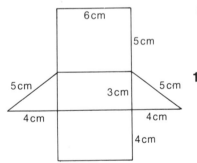

10 The diagram below shows a water trough whose cross-section is a semicircle. Taking π to be 22/7, work out, in m³, the volume of water that the trough holds when full.

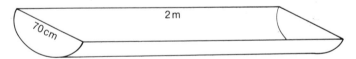

Exercise 33B

1 Find the area of a circle with
 a a radius of 8 cm, taking π to be 3,
 b a radius of 14 cm, taking π to be 22/7,
 c a diameter of 60 m, taking π to be 3.14,
 d a diameter of 1.8 m, taking π to be 3.

2 Find the areas of the following figures:

a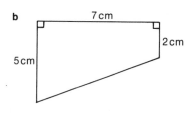

b

c the quadrilateral formed on graph paper by the points (1, 1), (3, 1), (1, 3) (−1, 3);

d the quadrilateral formed on graph paper by the points (−2, 1), (2, 2), (2, −4), (−2, −2).

3 The shaded shape on the left can be regarded as a rectangle from which four semicircles have been cut out. Taking π to be 3, work out

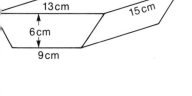

a the area of the rectangle,
b the area of the four semicircles,
c the area of the shaded shape.

4 Twelve metal prisms of cross-sectional area 38 cm² and length 4 cm are melted down and used to make a cuboid of length 15 cm, width 12.4 cm and height 9.5 cm. Work out
a the volume of the 12 prisms,
b the volume of the cuboid,
c the volume of metal left over.

5 The diagram on the left shows a container whose cross-section is an isosceles trapezium. Work out the volume of the container.

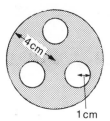

6 Three circles of radius 1 cm are cut out of a circle of radius 4 cm, as shown in the diagram below. Taking π to be 3.14, work out the remaining area.

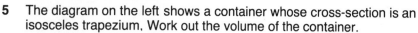

7 A cylindrical vessel has a cross-section which is a circle of radius 3.5 cm. Taking π to be 22/7, work out
a the area of the cross-section.
If 200 cm³ of water is poured into the vessel, work out
b the height the water will reach, to one decimal place.

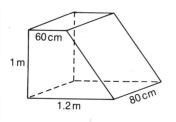

8 The diagram on the left shows a cabinet whose cross-section is a trapezium. Work out
a the area of the cross-section, in m²,
b the volume of the cabinet, in m³.

9 The following diagram represents the net of a triangular prism. The distances shown are in centimetres.,

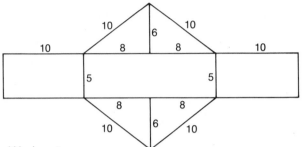

Work out
a the volume of the prism,
b the surface area of the prism.

10

3 cm

Some pots of jam have cross-sections which are circles of radius 3 cm, as shown above.
a The pots are stored, in a single layer, in a cupboard which is 90 cm long and 60 cm wide. How many pots will fit into the cupboard?
b Taking π to be 3.14, work out the cross-sectional area of one of the pots.
c Work out the area of cupboard floor space which is not used when as many pots as possible are stored in it.

Geometry

Simple angle properties, symmetry

1 Measure each of the following angles to the nearest degree, with a protractor:

a

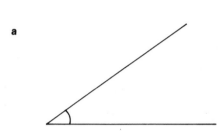

b

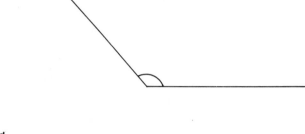

c

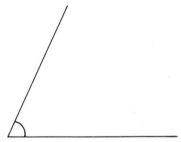

d

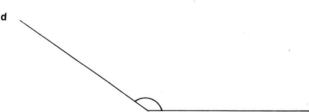

2 In each of the following cases work out the angle *x*:

a

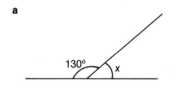

b

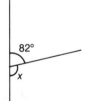

c

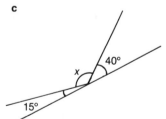

d

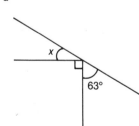

3 Sketch each of the following shapes and put in their axes of symmetry:

a

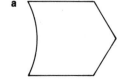

b

c

d

e

4 Work out the angle *w*:

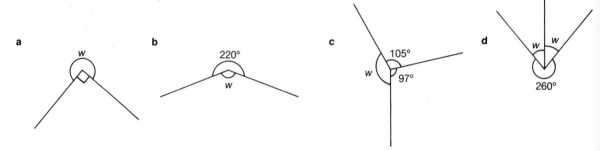

5 For each of the following capital letters state the number of axes of symmetry and also say whether or not the letter has rotational symmetry:

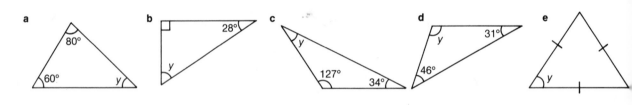

6 Work out the angle *y*:

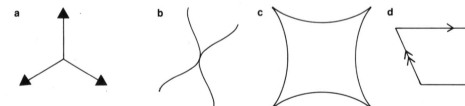

7 Each of the following figures has rotational symmetry. State the order of the symmetry in each case.

8 Using a scale of 1 cm to 1 unit on each axis, draw on graph paper the triangle whose vertices are A(0, 2), B(6, 0), C(4, 4).
   a Measure AC and BC to the nearest millimetre, and measure angle ACB.
   b What type of triangle is triangle ABC?
   c Work out angle BAC and angle ABC.

9 Work out angle *x* and angle *y* for each of the following figures:

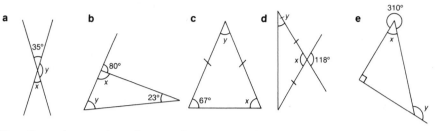

10 State the number of axes of symmetry of
  a an isosceles trapezium,
  b a rhombus,
  c a kite.

11 Sketch a square and put in all its axes of symmetry.

12 Work out angles *x* and *y*:

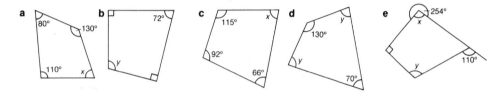

13 State the number of axes of symmetry and the order of the rotational symmetry of
  a a regular pentagon (5-sided polygon),
  b a regular octagon (8-sided polygon).

Exercise 34B

1 Measure each of the following angles, to the nearest degree, with a protractor:

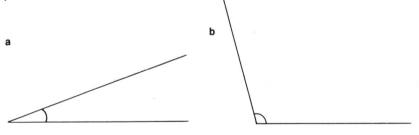

2 Without using a protractor, estimate the sizes of the following angles to the nearest 10 degrees:

123

3 Work out the angle *x*:

a 80° *x*

b 154° *x*

c 49° 73° *x*

d *x* *x* 50°

4 Sketch each of the following shapes and put in their axes of symmetry:

a

b

c

d

5 Work out the angle *y*:

a 135° *y*

b *y* 140°

c *y* *y* 120°

6 From the following set of capital letters, list
  a the letters with one axis of symmetry,
  b the letters with more than one axis of symmetry,
  c the letters with rotational symmetry.

B X F N W O E

7 Work out the angle *p*:

a *p* 85° 25°

b *p* 61°

c 49° *p* 97°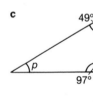

d *p* 33° 14°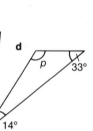

8 Say for each of the cases below whether or not the figure has rotational symmetry. If it does, state the order of the symmetry.

a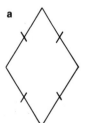

b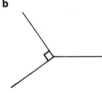

c

124

d a square,
e a rectangle which is not a square,
f a regular hexagon (6-sided polygon).

9 Work out angle *x* and angle *y* for each of the following figures:

a

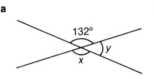

b

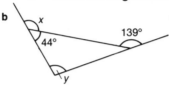

c

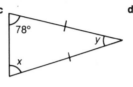

d

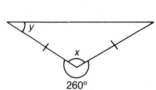

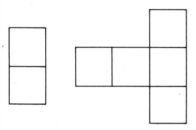

10 Draw diagrams in which the two figures on the left are put together in such a way as to make
a a figure with one axis of symmetry,
b a figure with two axes of symmetry.

11 Using a scale of 1 cm to 1 unit on each axis, draw on graph paper the quadrilateral whose vertices are A(1, 3), B(−1, 3), C(−2, 0), D(2, 0).
a What kind of quadrilateral is ABCD?

Put in two more points, P and Q, in such a way that the hexagon ABCPQD is symmetrical about the *x*-axis.
b State the coordinates of P and Q
c State two other symmetry properties of the hexagon ABCPQD.

12 Work out the angles *x* and *y*:

a

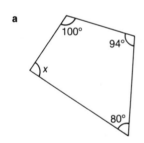

b

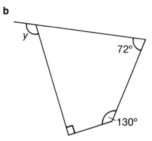

c

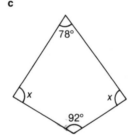

d

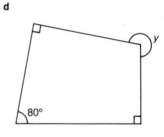

Further angle properties, polygons

Exercise 35A

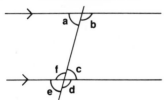

1 a Angles *a* and *c* are **alternate** angles. Name another pair of alternate angles.
b Name two pairs of **corresponding** angles.
c Angles *a* and *f* are **allied** angles (or **interior opposite** angles). Name another pair of allied angles.
d Given that angle *a* = 80°, write down the values of angles *c*, *e*, *f*.

2 Work out the angle x:

a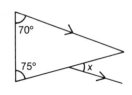

b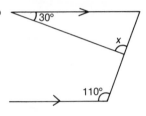

c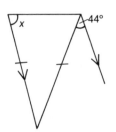

d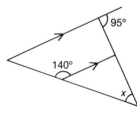

3 The diagram on the left shows a regular pentagon.
a Write down the sum of the five exterior angles shown.
b From your answer to **a**, work out the value of one exterior angle.
c Deduce the value of each interior angle of the pentagon.

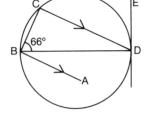

4 a Work out the value of each interior angle of a regular 9-sided polygon.
b Given that each exterior angle of a regular polygon is 36°, work out the number of sides in the polygon.
c Given that each interior angle of a regular polygon is 156°, work out the number of sides in the polygon.

5

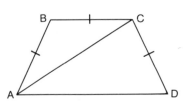

In the figure above, A, B, C, D are consecutive vertices of a regular hexagon. Work out angle BAC and angle ADC.

6 BD is a diameter of the circle on the left and DE is a tangent to it.
a Write down the value of angle BCD
b Work out angle ABD.
c Write down the value of angle BDE.
d Work out angle CDE.

7 All the diagrams below show semicircles. Work out angle x and angle y in each case.

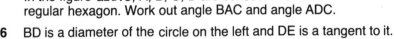

a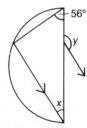

b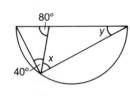

c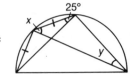

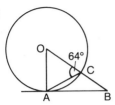

diagram 1

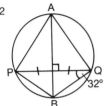

diagram 2

8 O is the centre of the circle in diagram 1 and AB is a tangent to it.
  a Name an isosceles triangle.
  b State the value of angle OAB.
  c Work out angle ABC.

9 In diagram 2, the lines AB and PQ are perpendicular and AB bisects PQ.
  a State one other fact about the line AB.
  b State the value of angle APB.
  c Work out angle APQ.
  d Work out angle BAQ.

10 AB is a tangent to the circle below and AD passes through the centre of the circle. AC = AD, as shown. Work out angle CAD.

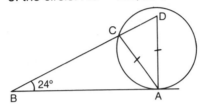

11 ABCDE is a regular pentagon inscribed in a circle, and DX is an axis of symmetry of the whole figure.
  a State the values of angle XED and angle EDC.
  b Work out angle EXD.
  c Work out angle BCX.

Level 2

Exercise 35B

1

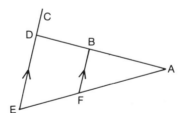

Name an angle which is
  a alternate to angle BDC,
  b corresponding to angle DEF,
  c allied to angle DBF.

2 Find the angles indicated by letters:

a

b

c

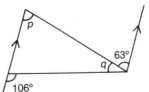

3 Work out
  a each exterior angle of a regular octagon (8-sided polygon),
  b each interior angle of a regular 12-sided polygon,
  c the sum of the interior angles of a regular hexagon,
  d the number of sides in a polygon whose interior angles are all 162°.

diagram 1

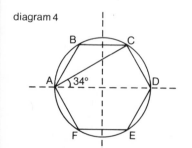

4 In diagram 1, ABCDE is a (non-regular) pentagon in which AX is an axis of symmetry. Work out
  a angle ABE,
  b angle AED.

5 A, B, C, D are consecutive vertices of a regular 10-sided polygon of centre O. Work out
  a angle AOB,
  b angle ACO,
  c angle ACD.

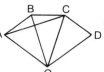

6 AB is a diameter of the circle shown in diagram 2 and QP is the perpendicular bisector of AC.
  a State the value of angle ACB.
  b What can you say about the point P?
  c Name two isosceles triangles.
  d Given that angle ABC = 64°, work out angles CAP and CPQ.

diagram 2

7 The diagrams below show semicircles. Work out the angles x and y.

a

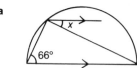

b

c

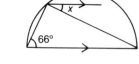

diagram 3

8 AD is an axis of symmetry of diagram 3 and CDE is a tangent to the circle.
Work out
  a angle BCD,
  b angle ADF.

9 AD is a diameter of the circle below and DC is a tangent to it.
AB = AE. Work out
  a angle DBE,
  b angle BCD.

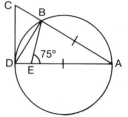

diagram 4

10 Diagram 4 shows a hexagon which is inscribed in a circle. The sides of the hexagon are not all equal but it has two axes of symmetry, as shown by the broken lines. Work out
  a angle ACD,   **c** angle AFE,
  b angle ACB,   **d** angle BAC.

128

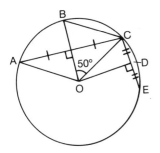

11 **a** Use the information given in the diagram on the left to explain why the point O must be the centre of the circle.
b Name two isosceles triangles.
c Work out angles OAC, OBC and ACB.

Bearings, maps, scale drawings

Exercise 36A

a 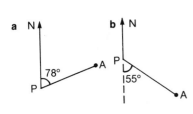 **b**

1 In each of diagrams **a** to **e** find the bearing of A from P:

2 The map shows some of the towns of Yorkshire. From the map, say which town is approximately
a due east of Selby,
b on a bearing of 040° from York,
c on a bearing of 120° from Leeds.
d on a bearing of 310° from Selby,
e on a bearing of 250° from Scunthorpe.

c 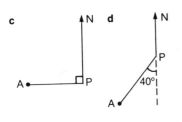 **d**

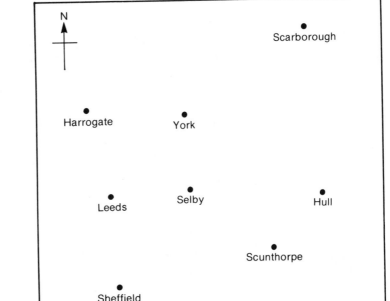

e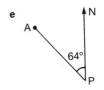

3

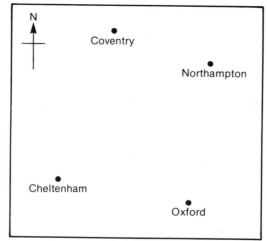

a Measure the distance on the map, in centimetres, between Paddington Station and Waterloo Station.

b Given that the scale of the map is 10 cm to 2 km, work out the actual distance between the stations.

c Measure the bearing of Waterloo Station from Paddington Station.

d Find the bearing of Paddington Station from Waterloo Station.

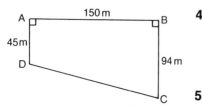

4 The figure ABCD on the left is a sketch (not drawn to scale) of a field.

a Using a scale of 1 cm to 10 m, make an accurate scale drawing of the field.

b Use your scale drawing to work out the actual length of CD, to the nearest metre.

5

a The actual distance between Oxford and Coventry is 50 miles. Measure this distance on the above map, and use your answer to work out the distance represented by 1 cm on the map.

b Use the map to work out the true distance between Oxford and Northampton.

c Use the map to work out the true distance between Coventry and Cheltenham.

6 Ms Kaminski drives 30 km due east from Netherfield to Barchester. Mrs Anderson starts at Norland, which is 45 km due north of Netherfield, and drives 48 km on a bearing of 120° to Hartfield.

a Letting 1 cm represent 5 km, make a scale drawing of these two journeys.

b Use your drawing to work out the distance between Barchester and Hartfield.

c Measure the bearing of Hartfield from Barchester.

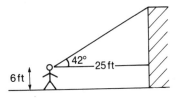

7 The diagram, on the left, shows a man looking at the top of a building. The man's eyes are 6 feet above the ground, as shown. Make a scale drawing and use it to estimate the height of the building as accurately as possible.

8 The diagram below, which represents three points on a map, is drawn to scale.

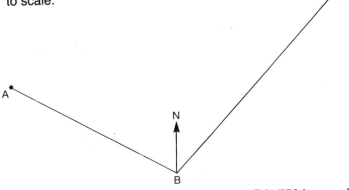

a Given that the actual distance from A to B is 750 km, work out the distance which is represented in the diagram by 1 cm.
b Work out the distance represented by BC.
c Measure the bearings of C from B and of A from B.

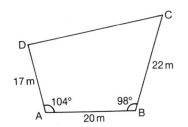

9 The figure ABCD on the left is a sketch of a garden. Using a scale of 1 to 200, make a scale drawing of the garden and use it to estimate the distances AC and BD to the nearest metre.

Exercise 36B

1 In each of diagrams **a** to **d** on the left, find the bearing of P from X:

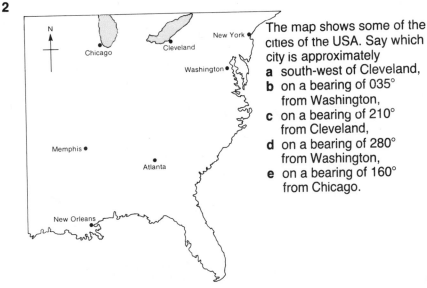

2 The map shows some of the cities of the USA. Say which city is approximately
a south-west of Cleveland,
b on a bearing of 035° from Washington,
c on a bearing of 210° from Cleveland,
d on a bearing of 280° from Washington,
e on a bearing of 160° from Chicago.

3

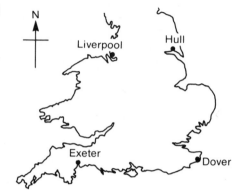

a Measure the distance on the above map, to the nearest millimetre, between Exeter and Dover.

b Given that the scale of the map is 1 cm to 100 km, work out the true distance between Exeter and Dover.

Use the map to work out also
c the true distance between Liverpool and Hull,
d the true distance between Hull and Exeter,
e the bearing of Dover from Liverpool, to the nearest 10°,
f the bearing of Exeter from Hull, to the nearest 10°.

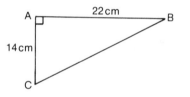

4 The triangle ABC is a sketch of a bracket for a shelf. Using a scale factor of 1/2, make a scale drawing of the bracket and use it to estimate
a the length BC,
b the angle ACB.

5

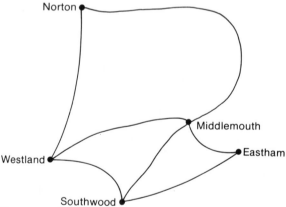

The map shows the principal roads linking five towns. Given that the scale of the map is 1 cm to 12 km, estimate the length of
a the shortest route from Southwood to Norton,
b the road directly linking Norton to Middlemouth,
c the journey from Eastham to Westland via Middlemouth.

6 A boy makes a journey in three stages. He goes 800 m on a bearing of 030°, then 350 m due east, then 420 m on a bearing of 135°. Make a scale drawing of this journey, and use it to work out
a the boy's final distance from his starting point,
b his final bearing from his starting point.

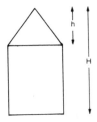

7 The figure on the left is a scale drawing of the end-view of a house.
   a Given that the true width of the house is 7.5 m, work out the length represented in the drawing by 1 cm.
   b Work out the height, *h*, of the roof of the house.
   c Work out the height, *H*, of the whole house.

8 The figure below is a sketch of a plot of land. Using a ruler and a compass, and taking a scale of 1 to 1000, make an accurate scale drawing of the plot and use it to estimate
   a the bearing of D from A,
   b the bearing of A from C,
   c the bearing of D from B.

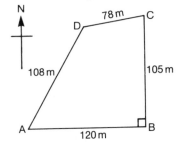

Congruence

Exercise 37A

1

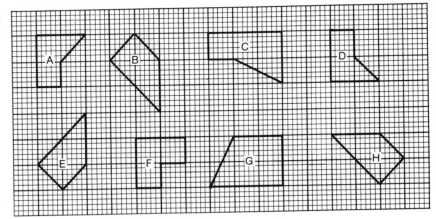

Which of the shapes shown above is/are congruent to
  a shape A?
  b shape B?

2 In each of the following cases there is just one pair of congruent figures. Name the congruent figures in each case.

a

P   Q   R.   S

b

W   X   Y   Z

c

K   L   M   N

3

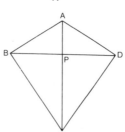

AC is an axis of symmetry of the figure on the left. Name three pairs of congruent triangles.

diagram 1

4 AD is an axis of symmetry of the figure in diagram 1. Name the figure which is congruent to
a the triangle ABM,
b the quadrilateral BCDM,
c the quadrilateral ABCF.

diagram 2

5 In diagram 2 name
a the triangle which is congruent to triangle ABG,
b the two triangles which are congruent to triangle ACG.

6 Draw on graph paper the triangle formed by the points A(6, 0), B(0, 6), C(1, 1). State the coordinates of a point D such that the triangles ABC, ABD are congruent.

7 Draw on graph paper the triangle formed by the points A(1, 0), B(2, 0), C(2, 2). State the coordinates of three points, D, E, F, none of them below the x-axis, such that the triangles BAD, EBC and FCB are all congruent to the triangle ABC.

8 Say in each of the following cases whether or not the triangles ABC, PQR are congruent. (Use the same scale on the two axes.)
a A is (0, 0), B is (1, 0) C is (0, 3); P is (0, 0), Q is (0, 1), R is (3, 0).
b A is (−1, 0), B is (1, 0), C is (0, 2); P is (0, −1), Q is (2, −1), R is (2, 1).
c A is (2, 0), B is (1, 2), C is (−1, 1); P is (1, 0), Q is (3, 1), R is (2, 3).

134

9 Say in each of the following cases whether or not the two triangles shown are congruent:

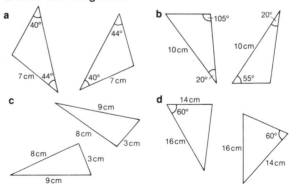

a

b

c

d

Level 2

Exercise 37B

1

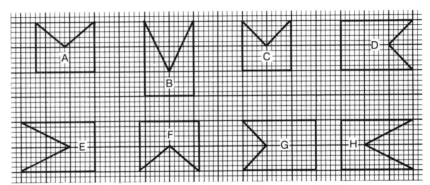

a From the above figure list three sets of congruent shapes.
b Name one shape which is not congruent to any of the others.

2 Pick out one pair of congruent figures from each of the sets of figures below.

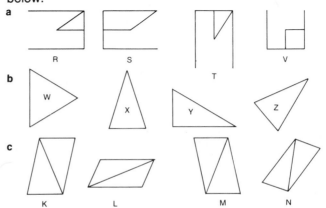

a

R   S   T   V

b

W   X   Y   Z

c

K   L   M   N

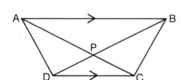

3 The figure on the left is an isosceles trapezium. Name three pairs of congruent triangles in the figure.

135

diagram 1

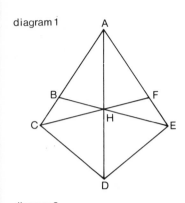

4 AD is an axis of symmetry of diagram 1. Name the figure which is congruent to
  a triangle AHC,
  b triangle ABE,
  c quadrilateral BCDE.

5 The figure ABCDE shown in diagram 2 is a regular pentagon. Name
  a two triangles which are congruent to triangle ABE,
  b one triangle which is congruent to triangle DEB.

6 Draw on graph paper the parallelogram whose vertices are A(4, 0), B(8, 0), C(12, 2), D(8, 2). The parallelogram PQRS is congruent to parallelogram ABCD. Given that P is the point (4, 6), Q is (4, 2) and R is (2, −2), find the coordinates of the point S.

diagram 2

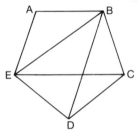

7 Draw on graph paper the triangle whose vertices are A(2, 1), B(6, 1), C(1, 3).
  a State the coordinates of a point D, above the x-axis, such that triangle BAD is congruent to triangle ABC.
  b State the coordinates of two points, E and F, below the x-axis, such that triangles ABE and BAF are both congruent to triangle ABC.

8 Say in each of the following cases whether or not the triangles ABC, PQR are congruent.
  a A is (2, 0), B is (0, 0), C is (−2, 1); P is (0, 2), Q is (0, 4), R is (2, 7).
  b A is (1, 2), B is (4, 2), C is (2, 3); P is (0, 1), Q is (0, −2), R is (−1, 0).
  c A is (2, −1), B is (4, −4), C is (−2, −2); P is (4, −2), Q is (8, −2), R is (3, 2).

9 Say in each of the following cases whether or not the two triangles shown are congruent:

a 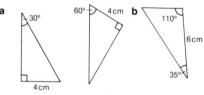 **b**

c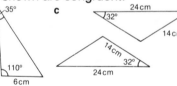

d **e**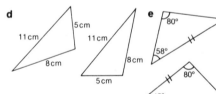

Similarity, enlargement

1

A

B 10 cm C

P Q 5 cm R

The triangles ABC, PQR shown above are similar.

a Express the ratio BC:QR as simply as possible.
b What is the ratio of AB to PQ?
c Given that AC = 12 cm, what is PR?

2 Using a scale of 1 cm to 1 unit on both axes, draw on graph paper the square whose vertices are A(2, 1), B(3, 1), C(3, 2), D(2, 2). Draw the image of the square under an enlargement of scale factor 2 with the origin as centre.
a Describe the image.
b State the coordinates of the images of A and B.

Draw also the image of the square ABCD under an enlargement of scale factor 3 with the point (4, 0) as centre.
c State the coordinates of the images of A and D.

3 Pick out one pair of similar figures from each of the following sets of figures:

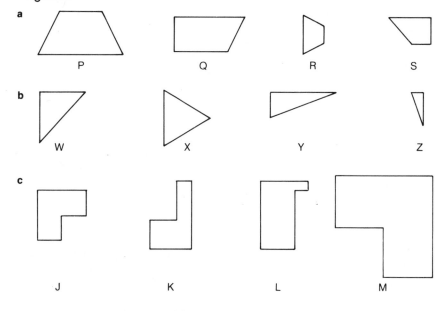

4

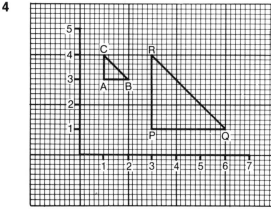

In the figure above the triangle PQR is an enlargement of triangle ABC.
a State the scale factor of the enlargement.
b State the coordinates of the centre of the enlargement.

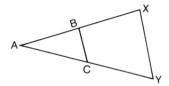

5 In the figure on the left the triangle AXY is an enlargement of triangle ABC. The centre of the enlargement is A, and the scale factor is 2.
   a Name two pairs of equal angles.
   b Given that BC = 8 cm, find XY.
   c Given that AY = 26 cm, find AC.
   d Given that BX = 12 cm, find AX.

6

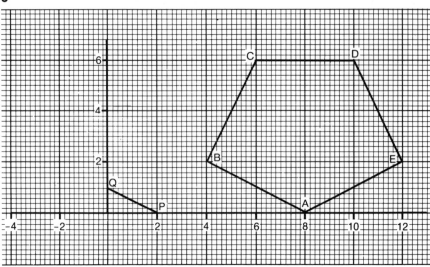

The above figure shows a pentagon ABCDE drawn on graph paper. Copy the figure onto your own graph paper and draw a similar pentagon PQRST, entirely above the x-axis, in which all the sides are of half the length of those in ABCDE. The first side PQ is drawn for you.
   a State the coordinates of R, S and T.
   b Regarding the pentagon ABCDE as an enlargement of PQRST, find the coordinates of the centre of the enlargement.

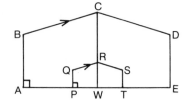

7 The line CW is an axis of symmetry of the figure on the left.
   a Name two similar pentagons in the figure.
   b Given that AP is twice the length of PW, state the ratio of any side in the large pentagon to the corresponding side in the smaller pentagon.
   c Given that PQ = 5 cm, find AB.
   d Given that CD = 24 cm, find QR.
   e Given that WT = 7 cm, find TE.
   f Regarding one of the similar pentagons as an enlargement of the other, name the centre and scale factor of the enlargement.

8 Taking a scale of 1 cm to 1 unit on each axis, draw an x-axis covering the range −6 to +8 and a y-axis covering the range 0 to +8. Draw the parallelogram whose vertices are A(0, 0), B(1, 0), C(2, 2), D(1, 2).
   a Draw the image of ABCD under an enlargement of centre A and scale factor 4. Label the image PQRS, with P being the image of A, Q the image of B, etc.
   b State the coordinates of Q and R.
   c Draw the image of ABCD under an enlargement of centre (3, 0) and

138

scale factor 2. Label the image KLMN, with K being the image of A,
L the image of B, etc.

d State the coordinates of L and N.

e State the scale factor and the centre of the enlargement which
maps the figure KLMN onto the figure PQRS.

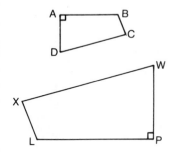

1 The two figures shown on the left are similar, the ratio of
corresponding sides being 1:2.

a Which point in the smaller figure corresponds to the point L?

b Which side in the larger figure corresponds to the side DC?

c Given that BC = 5 cm, which side in the larger figure can be found
and what is its value?

d Given that PL = 21 cm, which side in the smaller figure can be
found and what is its value?

2 Allowing a range of 0 to +12 on the x-axis, and a range of −3 to +7
on the y-axis, draw on graph paper the triangle whose vertices are
A(1, 1), B(3, 1), C(1, 2).

a Draw the image of triangle ABC under an enlargement of centre the
origin and scale factor 3.

b State the coordinates of the images of A, B and C under this
enlargement.

c Draw the image of triangle ABC under an enlargement of centre the
point (0, 2) and scale factor 4.

d State the coordinates of the images of A, B and C under this
enlargement.

3 Pick out a pair of similar figures from each of the following sets of
figures:

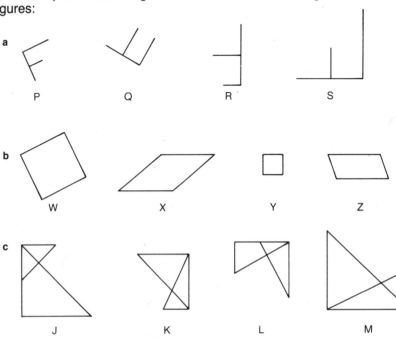

4

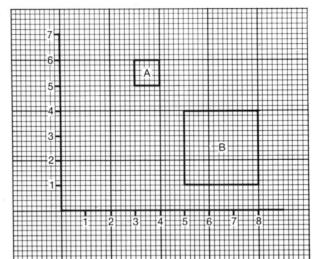

In the figure above the square B is an enlargement of the square A.
a State the scale factor of the enlargement.
b State the coordinates of the centre of the enlargement.

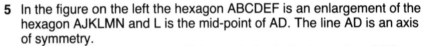

5 In the figure on the left the hexagon ABCDEF is an enlargement of the hexagon AJKLMN and L is the mid-point of AD. The line AD is an axis of symmetry.
a Name three trapeziums which are similar to the trapezium AJKL.
b Given that MN = 4 cm, find BC.
c Given that DC = 12 cm, find ML.
d State the centre and the scale factor of the enlargement.

6

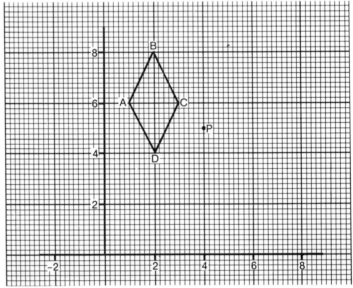

Copy the above quadrilateral onto your own graph paper and draw a similar quadrilateral PQRS, to the right of ABCD, in which each side is twice the corresponding side in ABCD. Take P to be the point (4, 5), as shown.

a What type of quadrilateral is ABCD?
b State the coordinates of Q, R and S.
c Regarding the quadrilateral PQRS as an enlargement of ABCD, find the coordinates of the centre of the enlargement.

7 In the figure on the left, the triangle AMN is an enlargement, with centre A, of the triangle ABC.
a State the scale factor of the enlargement.
b Work out BC.
c Work out AN.

8 Allowing a range of 0 to +12 on the x-axis and a range of 0 to +10 on the y-axis, draw on graph paper the trapezium whose vertices are A(8, 1), B(8, 2), C(6, 2), D(7, 1). Draw also the image PQRS of ABCD under an enlargement of centre (12, 0) and scale factor 2.
a State the coordinates of P, Q, R, S.

Draw now the image JKLM of PQRS under an enlargement of centre the origin and scale factor 2.
b State the coordinates of J, K, L, M.
c State the scale factor and the centre of the enlargement which maps ABCD onto JKLM.

Reflection, rotation, translation

Note: *In all the questions requiring graph paper, allow a range of −6 to +6 on both axes and use a scale of 1 cm to 1 unit.*

Exercise 39A

1

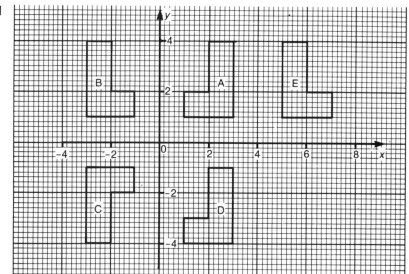

In the figure above, state the transformation which maps
a A to B,   **c** A to C,   **e** E to B.
b B to C,   **d** A to D,

2 Draw the triangle whose vertices are A(1, 1), B(4, 1), C(4, 2).
  a Reflect triangle ABC in the y-axis, labelling the image PQR (where P is the image of A, Q is the image of B, and R is the image of C). State the coordinates of P, Q, R.
  b Rotate triangle ABC through a half-turn (a turn of 180°) about the origin. Label the image LMN and state the coordinates of L, M, N.
  c State the single transformation which maps PQR onto LMN.

3 a A certain translation maps the point (1, 3) to the point (4, 5). What is the image of the point (0, 1) under this translation?
  b Another translation maps the point (2, 4) to the point (3, 2), What is the image of the point (−3, 0) under this translation?

4 Draw the triangle OAB, where O is the origin, A is the point (4, 0) and B is the point (4, 1).
  a Rotate triangle OAB through an anticlockwise quarter-turn (a turn of 90°) about O. State the coordinates of the images of A and B.
  b Rotate triangle OAB through a clockwise quarter-turn about the point (5, 0). State the coordinates of the images of O, A and B.

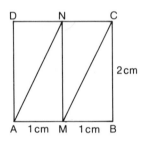

5 The figure on the left is a square which is divided into identical right-angled triangles. Describe the transformation which maps
  a triangle ADN onto triangle MNC,
  b rectangle AMND onto rectangle BMNC,
  c triangle ADN onto triangle NMA.

6 Draw the triangle whose vertices are A(−2, 2), B(−2, 3), C(−4, 2).
  a Rotate triangle ABC through a clockwise quarter-turn about the origin, letting the image be PQR. State the coordinates of P, Q, R.
  b Rotate triangle ABC through an anticlockwise quarter-turn about the origin, letting the image be LMN. State the coordinates of L, M, N.
  c State the single transformation which maps PQR onto LMN.

7

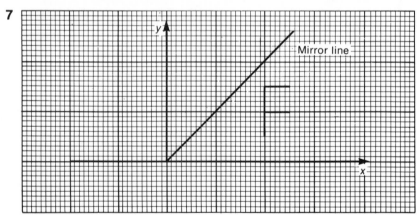

Copy the above diagram onto your own graph paper and reflect the F-shaped figure in the mirror line shown. Then reflect the image in the y-axis. By considering the original figure and the final image, state the single transformation which is equivalent to the two reflections you have performed.

8 Draw the triangle whose vertices are A(4, −1), B(6, −1), C(6, −2). Reflect this triangle in the x-axis, then reflect the image in the line

142

which is parallel to the x-axis and 3 units above it (the line $y = 3$).
Label the final image PQR and

a state the coordinates of P, Q, R.;

b describe the single transformation which maps ABC onto PQR.

9 Draw the triangle whose vertices are A(2, 2), B(5, 2), C(2, 3).

a Draw the image PQR of triangle ABC under a half-turn about the origin, and state the coordinates of P, Q, R.

b Draw the image LMN of triangle ABC under a translation of 6 units downwards and state the coordinates of L, M, N.

c Describe the single transformation which maps PQR onto LMN.

10 The figure on the left shows a square ABCD which is divided into smaller squares and right-angled triangles. Let the length AP = 1 unit. State the image of

a trapezium APJO under reflection in the line OJ,

b triangle DSL under reflection in the line AC,

c trapezium SMOD under a half-turn about O.

Describe also the transformation which maps

d trapezium OJQC onto trapezium OLRC,

e trapezium OCRL onto trapezium ODSM.

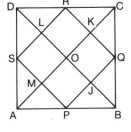

Exercise 39B

1

In the figure above, state the transformation which maps

a Q to T,   **d** T to S,

b R to P,   **e** Q to R,

c S to Q,   **f** S to R.

2

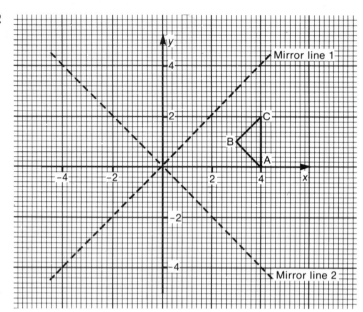

Copy the above diagram onto your own graph paper.
a Reflect triangle ABC in mirror line 1, labelling the image PQR. State the coordinates of P, Q, R.
b Reflect triangle ABC in mirror line 2, labelling the image LMN. State the coordinates of L, M, N.
c State the single transformation which maps PQR onto LMN.

3 a A certain translation maps the point (0, 3) to the point (4, 5). What is the image of the point (1, 2) under this translation?
b Another translation maps the point (3, −1) to the point (1, 0). What is the image of the point (0, −4) under this translation?

4 Draw the triangle whose vertices are A(2, 0), B(6, 0), C(6, 2).
a Draw the image PQR of triangle ABC under a half-turn about the origin. State the coordinates of P, Q, R.
b Draw the image AJK of triangle ABC under an anticlockwise quarter-turn about A. State the coordinates of J and K.
c Draw the image PMN of triangle PQR under a quarter-turn about P. State the coordinates of M and N.
d State the single transformation which maps AJK onto PMN.

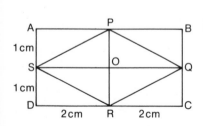

5 The figure on the left consists of identical right-angled triangles. Name the triangle or triangles onto which it is possible to map
a triangle SPO by reflection in an axis,
b triangle SDR by a translation,
c triangle PBQ by reflection in an axis.

Describe also the transformation which maps
d triangle ROQ to triangle SAP,
e triangle SOR to triangle QOR,
f triangle APS to triangle DRS,
g triangle APS to triangle OSP.

6 Draw the parallelogram whose vertices are A(2, 1), B(5, 1), C(6, 3), D(3, 3).

  a Draw the image PQRS of ABCD under a translation of 5 units to the left and 1 unit upwards. State the coordinates of P and R.

  b Draw the image JKLM of PQRS under a translation of 5 units downwards. State the coordinates of K and M.

  c State the single transformation which maps JKLM onto ABCD.

7 Draw the triangle whose vertices are A(6, 1), B(6, 2), C(4, 2).

  a Draw the image PQR of triangle ABC under reflection in the line which is parallel to the y-axis and 1 unit to the right of it (the line $x = 1$). State the coordinates of P, Q, R.

  b Draw the image JKL of triangle ABC under a translation of 2 units to the left. State the coordinates of J, K, L.

  c State the single transformation which maps PQR onto JKL.

8 Draw a pair of vertical lines 4 cm apart. Draw any simple figure slightly to the left of the left-hand line and reflect it in this line. Then reflect the image in the right-hand line.

  a By comparing your original figure and the final image state the single transformation which is equivalent to the pair of reflections you have performed.

  b What do you think the result would be if the two lines were 6 cm apart? (Check with a diagram if necessary.)

  c What would the result be if the lines were x cm apart?

9 Draw the triangle whose vertices are A(2, 1), B(4, 1), C(2, 2).

  a Draw the image PQR of triangle ABC under a half-turn about the point (0, 1). State the coordinates of P, Q, R.

  b Draw the image JKL of triangle PQR under a clockwise quarter-turn about the point $(-1, -1)$. State the coordinates of J, K, L.

  c State the single transformation which maps ABC onto JKL.

Trigonometry, Pythagoras' Theorem

Note: *In all the exercises in this section, give angles to one decimal place and lengths to three significant figures (unless they come out exactly).*

Quick revision exercise 40

1 Find x:

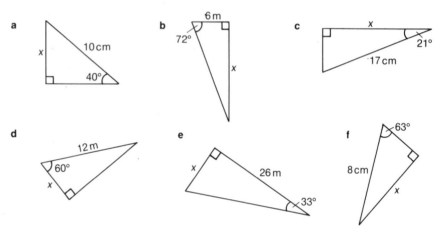

a 10 cm, x, 40°

b 6 m, 72°, x

c x, 21°, 17 cm

d 12 m, 60°, x

e x, 26 m, 33°

f 63°, 8 cm, x

2 Find θ:

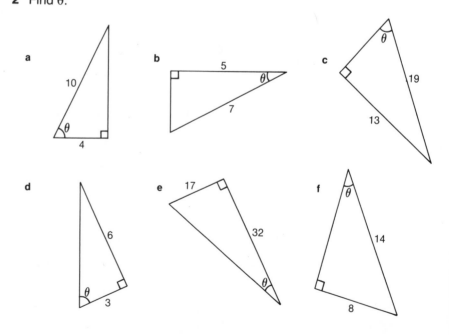

a 10, θ, 4

b 5, θ, 7

c θ, 19, 13

d 6, θ, 3

e 17, 32, θ

f θ, 14, 8

3 Find *x* by using Pythagoras' theorem:

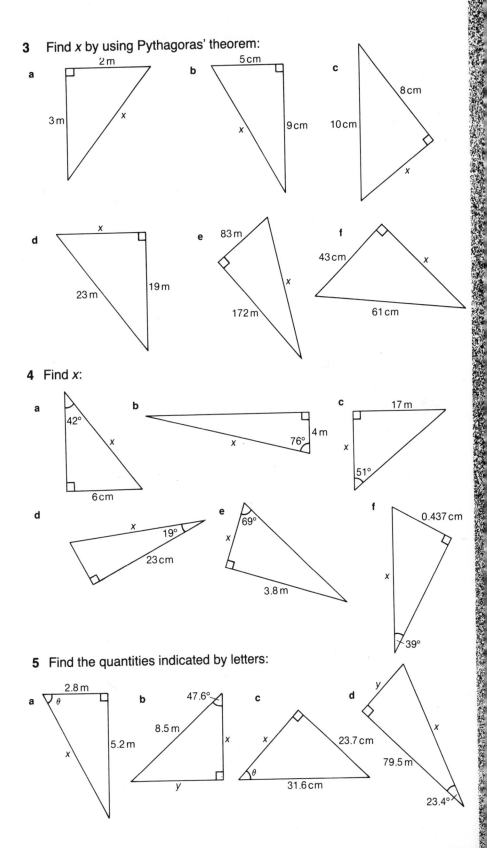

a 2 m, 3 m, *x*

b 5 cm, 9 cm, *x*

c 8 cm, 10 cm, *x*

d *x*, 23 m, 19 m

e 83 m, 172 m, *x*

f 43 cm, 61 cm, *x*

4 Find *x*:

a 42°, *x*, 6 cm

b 76°, 4 m, *x*

c 17 m, 51°, *x*

d *x*, 19°, 23 cm

e 69°, *x*, 3.8 m

f 0.437 cm, *x*, 39°

5 Find the quantities indicated by letters:

a 2.8 m, θ, 5.2 m, *x*

b 47.6°, 8.5 m, *x*, *y*

c *x*, θ, 23.7 cm, 31.6 cm

d *y*, *x*, 79.5 m, 23.4°

147

6 Find the quantities indicated by letters, in each case starting by drawing one or more perpendiculars:

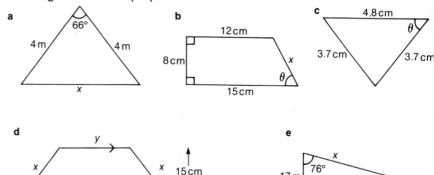

Practical applications of trigonometry

Note: *Give bearings to the nearest degree.*

Exercise 41A

1 A car is driven 50 km due east from a point P to a point Q, then 20 km due south to a point R. Sketch the triangle PQR and work out
  a the final distance PR of the car from its starting point,
  b the final bearing of the car from its starting point.

2 It is planned to work out the height of a tower by measuring the angle of elevation of its highest point from a point on the ground. In the diagram below AT represents the tower and P is the point on the ground. Use the data given in the diagram to work out the height of the tower.

3 The area of the parallelogram below is required. Use trigonometry to find the height of the parallelogram, and then work out its area.

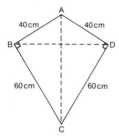

4 The figure ABCD on the left is a sketch of a kite that a boy is making. Work out
  a the length of the diagonal AC,
  b angle BAD,
  c the length of the diagonal BD.

148

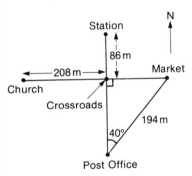

5 The diagram on the left shows some of the main features of a village. The station is due north of the crossroads and the Post Office, while the church, crossroads and market are on an east–west line. Work out
   a the distance of the station from the church,
   b the bearing of the station from the church,
   c the distance of the Post Office from the crossroads,
   d the bearing of the Post Office from the church,
   e the distance of the market from the station.

6 From the top of a cliff the angle of depression of a boat is found to be 27°. It is known that the height of the cliff is 60 m. Work out the distance of the boat from the bottom of the cliff.

7 When a train stops at a city station, it is 5 km due south of the city's cathedral. The train moves away from the station on a bearing of 050°, as shown on the left.
   a When the train is due east of the cathedral, how far has it travelled from the station?
   b Mark on your own diagram the point at which the train is at its shortest distance from the cathedral. Work out this distance.

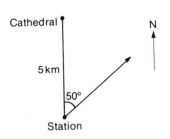

8

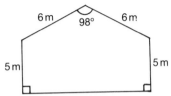

The figure shows the end view of a building. Work out
   a the width of the building,
   b the height of the building.

9 In diagram 1 on the left, CD represents a window in a vertical wall. From a point A on the ground, which is 5 m from the wall, the angles of elevation of C and D are 30° and 40°, respectively. Work out
   a the height of the base of the window, BC,
   b the height of the top of the window, BD,
   c the vertical length of the window, CD.

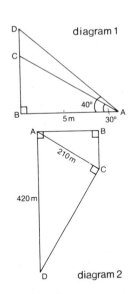

10 Diagram 2 on the left represents a plot of land. The plot has the form of a trapezium made up of two right-angled triangles, as shown. Work out
   a angle DAC,
   b the length CD,
   c the length BC,
   d the perimeter of the plot,
   e the area of the plot.

Level 2

Exercise 41B

1 Simone sets out from her home and walks 550 m on a bearing of 073°. How far east of her home is she at the end of the journey?

2 A ladder of length 12 m leans against a vertical wall with its foot on horizontal ground at a distance of 2.5 m from the wall. Work out
   a the height of the top of the ladder,
   b the inclination of the ladder to the ground.

3 The angle of elevation of the top of a post from a certain point is 41°. As shown below, this point is 6 feet above the ground and a horizontal distance of 17 feet from the post. Work out the height of the post.

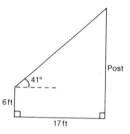

4

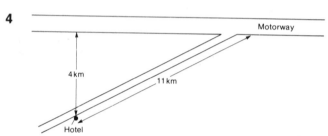

A car leaves a motorway which runs east–west and travels 11 km on another road to an hotel. The hotel is 4 km due south of the motorway. Work out the bearing on which the car travels to the hotel.

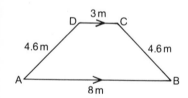

5 The figure ABCD on the left, which is an isosceles trapezium, represents the end view of the roof of a house. Sketch the figure and add two vertical lines to it. Then work out
   a the vertical depth of the roof (the distance between AB and DC),
   b the inclination of AD and BC to the horizontal,
   c the area of the figure ABCD.

6 The area of a regular hexagon of side 12 cm is required. To work this out, the hexagon is divided up into a rectangle and four right-angled triangles, as shown on the left.

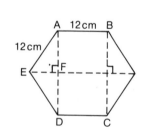

State the size of angle AEF and hence work out
   a EF,
   b AF,
   c the area of triangle AEF.
   d the area of rectangle ABCD,
   e the area of the whole hexagon.

7 Pythagoras' theorem shows that a rectangle of length 12 cm and width 5 cm has a diagonal of length 13 cm. Without using a calculator, find the length of the diagonal of a rectangle with
   a length 120 cm and width 50 cm,
   b length 24 cm and width 10 cm,
   c length 1.2 cm and width 0.5 cm,
   d length 6 cm and width 2.5 cm.

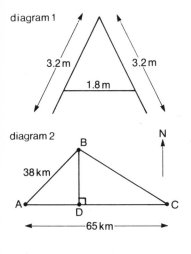

diagram 1

3.2 m   3.2 m

1.8 m

diagram 2

B

38 km

A

D

65 km

C

N

8 Diagram 1 on the left represents a pair of step ladders, each of length 3.2 m, which are held in position by a horizontal rope of length 1.8 m. The points of attachment of the rope are a quarter of the way up each ladder. Work out the angle between the two ladders.

9 Diagram 2 on the left shows the positions of four towns, A, B, C, D. Town B is exactly northeast of town A and due north of town D, while towns A, D and C are on an east–west line. Work out
a the distance between B and D,
b the distance between B and C,
c the bearing of B from C.

10 From the top of a vertical tower AB, of height 25 m, the angle of depression of a point P, which is on the ground and due east of the tower, is 37°. Work out
a the distance AP of P from the foot of the tower.

Another point Q, which is also on the ground and due east of the tower, is 20 m from P. Work out
b the angle of depression of Q from the top of the tower.

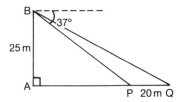

B
37°
25 m
A
P 20 m Q

GCSE Specimen Papers

All the questions in the papers which follow are taken from the specimen papers issued by the GCSE examining groups. The system used by most of the groups is that Level 1 candidates attempt Papers 1 and 2, while Level 2 candidates attempt Papers 2 and 3. The papers below are assembled in accordance with this system.

The examining groups are indicated by the following abbreviations:

LEAG = London and East Anglian Group
SEG = Southern Examining Group
MEG = Midland Examining Group
NEA = Northern Examining Association

Paper 1 (Approximately 1½ hours)

1   What is the next whole number after 3099?   *(LEAG)*

2   What fraction of the shape on the left is shaded?   *(NEA)*

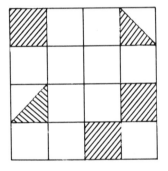

3   A model of a tank is 6.5 cm long. The scale of the model is 1 to 72. Calculate the length of the tank in metres.   *(MEG)*

4

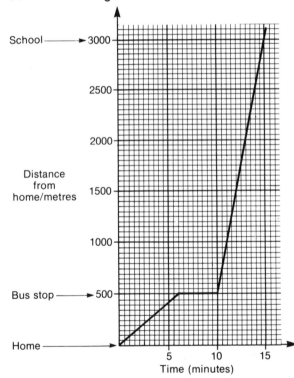

The graph shows Jane's journey from home to school. She walked from home to a bus stop, waited, then caught the bus to school.
   a How long did it take her to walk to the bus stop?
   b How long did she wait at the bus-stop?
   c How far from home was she after 13 minutes?
   d How many kilometres is it from the bus stop to school?   *(MEG)*

5 Work out the value of $2L + 2B$ when $L = 12$ and $B = 9$. *(NEA)*

6 Put the correct numbers in the boxes:

(LEAG)

a

```
   □  5  □
   7  1  4  +
─────────────
1  0  □  1
```

b

```
5  □  4  7
2  8  □  5  −
─────────────
□  7  3  □
```

7

SCONES
8 oz plain flour
1 teaspoon salt
1 teaspoon bicarbonate of soda
2 teaspoons cream of tartar
$1\frac{1}{2}$ oz margarine
About $\frac{1}{4}$ pint milk

This recipe is enough for 8 scones.
a How much flour is needed for 12 scones?
b How much milk is needed for 12 scones? *(NEA)*

8 The chart below shows the distances between six towns in miles.

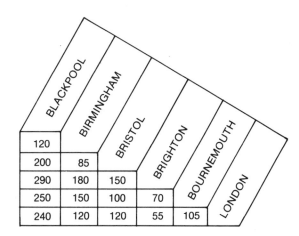

A lorry driver travels from Birmingham to Bristol and then on to Brighton at an average speed of 45 m.p.h. How long does her journey take? (Give your answer to the nearest hour.) *(SEG)*

9 Write down the next two numbers in the following patterns:
a 1, 4, 7, 10, 13, . . .
b 3, 6, 12, 24, 48, . . .
c 1, 4, 9, 16, 25, . . . *(MEG)*

10 A school decides to have a disco from 8 p.m. to midnight. The price of the tickets will be 20p. The costs are as follows:

disco and DJ, £25
hire of hall, £5 an hour
200 cans of soft drinks at 15p each
200 packets of crisps at 10p each
printing of tickets, £5

a What is the total cost of putting on the disco?
b How many tickets must be sold to cover the cost?
c If 400 tickets are sold, all the drinks are sold at 20p each and all the packets of crisps at 12p each, calculate the profit or loss the school finally makes. *(NEA)*

11

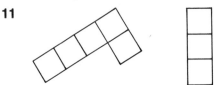

a Use the two shapes above to make a shape which has 2 lines of symmetry (mirror lines).
b Use the two shapes to make a shape which has only one line of symmetry. *(LEAG)*

12 In the diagram on the left, XY is a straight line. Calculate the size of the angle marked with a question mark. *(NEA)*

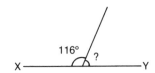

13 The graph below is to convert English Pounds to Austrian Schillings.

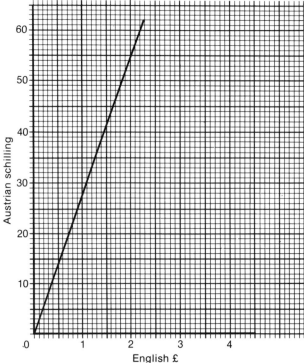

English £

a Change £2.20 into Austrian Schillings.
b How much English money should you get for 45 Schillings?
c Calculate the number of Austrian Schillings you should get for £8.00. *(SEG)*

14 **a** On Monday at 6.00 a.m. the temperature was −6°C and at 8.00 a.m. it was −1°C. By how much had the temperature risen?
b By 10.00 a.m. on the same day the temperature was 12°C higher than at 8.00 a.m. What was the temperature at 10.00 a.m.? *(MEG)*

154

15

The above map shows some of the towns in England, Scotland and Wales. It is drawn on a scale of 1 cm to 100 km. The direction of North is shown. Use your ruler and/or protractor to answer the following questions.

a Which town marked is approximately due East of Oxford?

b What is the distance between Liverpool and Brighton?

c Which town is approximately 360 km on a bearing of 132° from Carlisle?

d What is the bearing of Norwich from Cardiff? *(MEG)*

16 The following is an extract from the TV programmes for Wednesday 19 June.

7.15 p.m.	Blackpool Holiday Show
8.20 p.m.	Film of the Week
10.05 p.m.	News
10.15 p.m.	Country Music (repeat of last Wednesday's programme)
11.00 p.m.	Athletics Championships
11.25 p.m.	International Ice-Skating
11.55 p.m.	News
12.15 p.m.	Close Down

a How long does the film last?

b Which programme lasts just over an hour?

c On what date was Country Music first shown?

d If someone watches all the above programmes, how long will they have been watching? *(NEA)*

17 A game is played with two spinners. You add the two numbers to get the score.

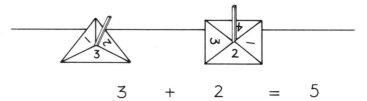

$$3 \quad + \quad 2 \quad = \quad 5$$

This score is shown on the table of results below.

	1	**2**	**3**
1			
2			5
3			
4			

a Complete the table to show all the possible scores.
b What is the probability of scoring 4?
c What is the probability of scoring an even number ?   *(LEAG)*

18 In a random survey in Lutonbury the ages of 30 people were:

a Copy and complete this table of results.

Age	Tally	Frequency
1–10		2
11–20		7
21–30		
31–40		
41–50		
51–60		
61–70		
71–80		
Over 80		
	TOTAL	30

b How many people were aged 51 to 60?

c Copy and complete the bar chart to show the information in the table.

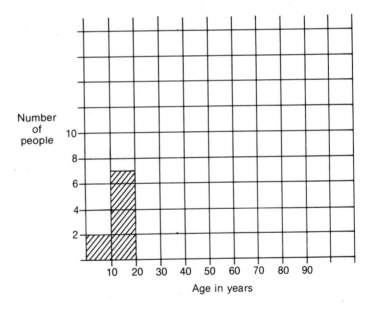

d (i) What fraction of those surveyed are aged 51 to 60?

(ii) If this is typical of 30 000 people in Lutonbury how many of the population are aged 51 to 60?

(iii) What percentage of the population is aged 31 to 40?

(LEAG)

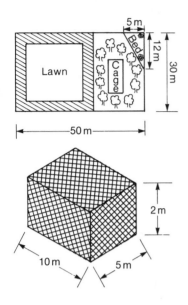

19 The sketch on the left shows a garden plot 50 m by 30 m. It has a square lawn surrounded by a path 1 m wide (shaded) It also has a triangular flower bed with sides 13 m, 12 m and 5 m.
  a Find the area of the whole plot.
  b Find the length of the lawn.
  c Find the area of the path.
  d Find the area of the triangular flower bed.

There is a fruit cage 10 m long, 5 m wide and 2 m high in the vegetable plot:
  e Calculate the volume of the cage.
  f The cage does not have a base. Calculate the area of netting needed to make it. *(SEG)*

Paper 2 (Approximately 1½ hours)

1 Write the following numbers in order of size, smallest first:

  0.66   0.625   0.088   0.667   *(NEA)*

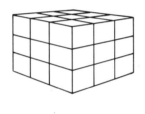

2 On the left is a 3 × 3 × 3 block made from small cubes. Rosa painted the outside of it red and then took the block to pieces.
  a How many cubes did she find with 3 faces painted red?
  b How many cubes did she find with 2 faces painted red?
  c How many cubes did she find with no faces painted red? *(LEAG)*

3 Three of the interior angles of a quadrilateral are 49°, 121° and 127°. What is the size of the fourth angle? *(SEG)*

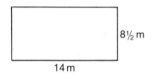

4 A man wants to put fertilizer on his lawn (shown on the left). His garden book tells him to use 50 g of fertilizer for each square metre.
  a How much fertilizer does he need?
  b At the shop, he can get only one packet of fertilizer which weighs 5 kg. He spreads this over the lawn. On average, how much fertilizer is there on each square metre of the lawn? *(NEA)*

5

		Mondays to Saturdays			
Norwich	d.	06 40	07 42	07 50	08 40
Wymondham	d.	06 56		08 05	08 56
Spooner Row	d.			08 09	
Attleborough	d.	07 03		08 14	09 03
Eccles Road	d.			08 20	
Harling Road	d.			08 25	09 13
Thetford	a.	07 21	08 16	08 35	09 24

d. means depart;   *a.* means arrive

The above shows part of the timetable of trains travelling from Norwich to Thetford.
  a If you live in Norwich, which is the first train you can catch after 7 a.m. which will take you to your work in Harling Road?
  b On another occasion you have to meet an important visitor on Thetford Station at 08.30. Which train should you catch in Norwich to be there in reasonable time to meet him? *(LEAG)*

158

6 Errol thinks of a number, doubles it and adds 12. The answer is 20. What number did Erroll think of? *(NEA)*

7 Whiteside toothpaste is sold in three sizes:

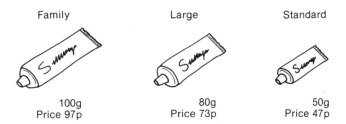

Family   Large   Standard

100g   80g   50g
Price 97p Price 73p Price 47p

Which size is the best value for money? Describe how you reached your answer. *(SEG)*

8 Emily was seriously ill in hospital, and it was necessary to keep a constant watch on her temperature. She was therefore connected to a machine which measured her temperature and drew the following graph:

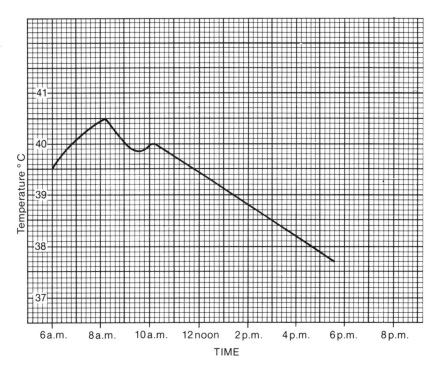

a At what time was her temperature highest?
b What was this highest temperature?
c At what time did her temperature start to go down steadily and not rise again?
d Emily's normal temperature is 37°C. For how long was her temperature more than 2°C higher than this?
e Emily's temperature continues to fall at the same rate. At what time will it be back at normal? *(LEAG)*

159

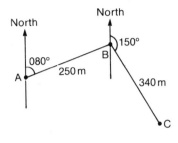

9 A wheel is turning at 15 revolutions per minute.
  a How many revolutions does it make each hour?
  b How many minutes does it take to make 6000 revolutions? *(NEA)*

10 The sketch on the left shows three posts A, B and C on a building site. It also shows some lengths and some bearings.
  a Using the distances and bearings shown on the diagram make a scale drawing to show the positions of A, B and C. Use a scale of 1 cm to represent 50 m.
  b Join AC and measure its length to the nearest millimetre.
  c What is the distance on the building site between the two posts A and C?
  c Measure and write down the size of angle BAC.
  e What is the bearing of C from A?
  f What is the bearing of A from C?
  g By drawing further lines on your scale drawing, find how far the post C is east of the post A. *(SEG)*

11 John's cycle has a radius of 1 ft.
  a Calculate the circumference of John's front wheel. (Take π to be 3.14.)
  b Calculate how far John has cycled when the front wheel has rotated 70 times.
  c Give this distance to the nearest hundred feet. *(SEG)*

12 A small business company employs 15 people. They are a manager, a foreman, 4 skilled workers and 9 unskilled workers. Their wages are shown in the following table:

Manager £12 000 per year	
Foreman £585 per month	12 payments per year
A skilled worker £105 per week	52 payments per year
An unskilled worker £75 per week	

  a How much does the foreman earn per year?
  b How much does each unskilled worker earn per year?
  c How much does the company pay all 9 unskilled workers in a year?
  d What is the company's total wage bill for the year (all 15 employees)?

  In negotiations about this year's pay rise, the company and the Union of Workers fail to decide between a 5% pay rise or a flat-rate increase. The flat-rate increase would be calculated by sharing £3900 equally among the 15 employees.
  e How much extra money per year would a 5% rise cost the company?
  f What will be the new yearly wage of a foreman if this 5% offer is accepted?
  g What will be the new yearly wage of an unskilled worker if the flat-rate increase is accepted? *(LEAG)*

13 Using a scale of 1 cm to 1 unit on both axes, plot and label on graph paper the points P(4, 3), Q(9, 3), R(6, 7), S(1, 7). Join the points with straight lines to form the 4-sided figure PQRS.

a Measure the length of QR.
b Write down a fact about the lengths of the sides of PQRS.
c Write down a fact about the angles of PQRS.
d Write down a fact about the symmetry of PQRS.
e Find the area of triangle PQR.   (NEA)

14 When Diana Wales attends meetings her car expenses are worked
out as follows:
For journeys of 50 miles or less

$$\text{Amount} = £\frac{24N}{100}$$

For journeys of more than 50 miles

$$\text{Amount} = £12 + £\frac{(N-50)\,12}{100}$$

N is the number of miles travelled.

a How much will she be paid for a journey of 26 miles?
b How much will she be paid for a journey of 75 miles?
c How much will she be paid per mile for journeys of less than 50
miles?   (NEA)

15 Midland Motors hire out lorries. Some of their hire charges are shown
in the table below.

Distance travelled (km)	0	150	300
Hire charge (£)	60	150	240

Taking a scale of 2 cm to 50 km on the horizontal axis, and a scale of
2 cm to £20 on the vertical axis, plot the points representing these
charges on graph paper and join them with a straight line. Use this
graph to find
a the hire charge for a lorry to travel 100 km,
b the distance travelled by a lorry for which the hire charge is £210.

Cambridge Carriers also hire out lorries. Some of their charges are
given in the following table.

Distance travelled (km)	50	100	200	300
Hire charge (£)	160	170	190	210

c On the same graph paper as used for Midland Motors, plot the
points representing these charges and join them with a straight line.
Hence find the distance for which Midland Motors and Cambridge
Carriers have the same hire charge.   (MEG)

16 The following are the first six numbers, written in order of size, of a pattern:

4,   13,   28,   49,   76,   109

a Which of these numbers are (i) odd numbers, (ii) square numbers, (iii) prime numbers?

b The difference between the first and second numbers, that is 13 − 4, is 9; between the second and third it is 15; between the third and the fourth it is 21. Work out the difference between (i) the fourth and the fifth numbers, (ii) the fifth and the sixth numbers.

c By considering your answers in **b**, find the seventh and eighth numbers of the pattern. Explain how you reached this decision.

d Use the method you have described to write down the next two terms in the following pattern:

1,   4,   12,   25,   43,   66

(SEG)

17 In the diagram on the left, V represents a village, J represents a motorway junction and S represents a service station.

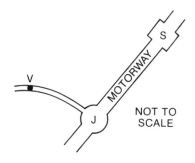

NOT TO SCALE

a A car started at V and travelled along the road from V to J, a distance of 24 km, at an average speed of 48 km/h. Find the time taken, in hours, to travel from V to J.

b The car then travelled along the motorway from J to S, a distance of 156 km, at an average speed of 104 km/h. Find the time taken, in hours, to travel from J to S.

c Calculate the total distance travelled from V to S.

d Calculate the total time taken for the journey from V to S.

e Calculate the average speed of the car for the journey from V to S.

f The car started from V at a quarter past eleven. At what time did it arrive at S?

(MEG)

Paper 3 (Approximately 2 hours)

1 **a** The attendance at United's last match was 15 374. Write the attendance figure correct to three significant figures.

b The attendance at City's last match was given as 24 000, correct to the nearest 100. Write down the lowest and highest possible attendances.

(MEG)

2 The diagram on the left shows a rectangular allotment garden, 30 m by 10 m. It contains a fruit section in the shape of a circle of diameter 8 m. In the rest of the garden vegetables are grown.

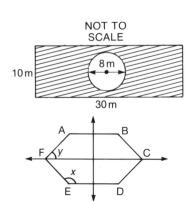

NOT TO SCALE

a Taking π to be 3, find the area of the circular fruit section.

b Find the area of the shaded vegetable section.

(MEG)

3 The distance of the earth from the sun is 93 million miles. Express this distance in standard form.

(NEA)

4 The diagram on the left shows a hexagon with just two lines of symmetry. Find the value of x when y is 25°

(SEG)

5 The graph of the line with equation $5x + 12y = 60$ cuts the x-axis at A and the y-axis at B.

   a Find the coordinates of A.
   b Find the coordinates of B.
   c Calculate the length of AB.   *(MEG)*

6

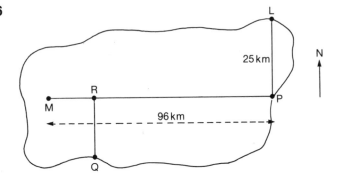

The above diagram is a sketch map of an island. The lighthouse L is 25 km due north of Portpearl (P) and the Mount (M) is 96 km due west of Portpearl.

   a Calculate, to the nearest kilometre, the distance of the lighthouse from the Mount.

   b Calculate, to the nearest degree, the size of angle LMP and hence find the bearing of L from M.

The Quay (Q) is 20 km from the Mount on a bearing of 125°. The Rooftop Hotel (R) is due north of the Quay and due east of the Mount.

   c Draw a rough sketch of triangle MRQ and mark on it the length of MQ and the size of each of its angles.

   d Calculate, in kilometres to one decimal place, the distance of the Rooftop Hotel from (i) the Mount, (ii) Portpearl.   *(LEAG)*

7 v, u, a and t are related by the formula $v = u + at$.
   a *Find v when $u = 60$, $a = -10$ and $t = 4$.*
   b Find u when $v = 55$, $a = 4$ and $t = 12$.
   c Express a in terms of v, u and t.   *(MEG)*

8 Ravinder's father said he would reward Ravinder if his mean (average) mark for his six examinations was 65 or more. After five examinations Ravinder's average mark was exactly 60. For his sixth examination Ravinder got 84. Find his final mean (average) mark. *(MEG)*

9 Alan, Brian and Charles stake £5 on the football pools each week. Alan pays £1, Brian £1.50 and Charles £2.50. They agree to share any winnings in proportion to their payments. One week they win £375. Find Brian's share of this.   *(NEA)*

10   **a** Given that $y = (x - 1)^2$, copy and complete the following table.

x	−1	−0.5	0	0.5	1	1.5	2	2.5	3
y		2.25	1	0.25		0.25	1		4

   b Using a scale of 4 cm to represent 1 unit on each axis, draw the graph of $y = (x - 1)^2$ for values of x from -1 to 3 inclusive.

c By drawing a tangent, estimate the gradient of the graph at the point (2,1).

d Use your graph to find the values of x for which $(x - 1)^2 = 3$.

(MEG)

11 **a** Express $\dfrac{3^2 \times 3^4}{3^8}$ as a single power of 3.

b State your answer as a fraction. *(NEA)*

12 Using a scale of 1 cm to 1 unit on each axis, and letting both x and y cover the range -6 to $+6$, draw on graph paper the triangle T whose vertices have coordinates of (1, 1), (5, 1) and (5, 3).

a A is the image of triangle T after it has been rotated through a half-turn about the origin (0, 0). Draw A and state the coordinates of its vertices.

b B is the image of triangle T after it has been rotated through a half-turn about the point (3, 0). Draw B and state the coordinates of its vertices.

c C is the image of triangle T after it has been reflected in the y-axis. Draw C and state the coordinates of its vertices.

d Describe fully the transformation which maps A onto B.

e Describe fully the transformation which maps A onto C. *(LEAG)*

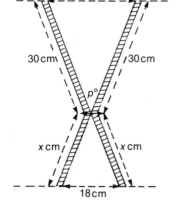

13 The diagram on the left shows the end view of a household newspaper rack.

a Use the information given in the diagram to calculate the size of the angle $p°$, giving the answer correct to the nearest degree.

b Calculate the value of x, giving your answer correct to one decimal place. *(NEA)*

14 Two bags contain coloured beads.

Bag A contains 3 blue beads and 1 red bead.

Bag B contains 3 blue beads and 3 red beads.

Two draws are made, at random in each case.

Draw 1—a bead is taken from Bag A and put in Bag B.

Draw 2—a bead is taken from Bag B.

Copy the tree diagram below and write the appropriate probabilities on the branches. *(NEA)*

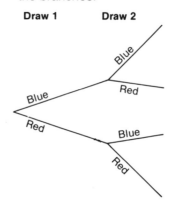

164

15 In her will, Granny leaves all her money to be shared by her three grandchildren. Anne is to have £400 more than Beatrice. Clarissa is to have three times as much as Beatrice.
   a If Beatrice receives £x, then Anne receives £(x + 400). Write an expression for the amount Clarissa receives in terms of x.
   b Suppose Clarissa receives £300. How much does Anne receive?
   c When Granny died, Anne and Clarissa received the same amount of money. How much did Granny leave? *(SEG)*

16

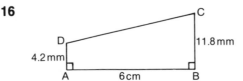

The above diagram shows the cross-section ABCD of a plastic door wedge.
   a Write down, in cm, the length of BC.
   b Calculate, in cm², the area of the cross-section ABCD.
   c Given that the wedge is of width 3 cm, calculate the volume, in cm³, of plastic required to make (i) 1 wedge, (ii) 1 000 000 wedges. *(LEAG)*

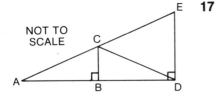

17 In the diagram on the left, triangle ADE is the image of triangle ABC after an enlargement of scale factor +2, using A as the centre of enlargement. Angles ABC and ADE are right angles.
   a Write down the length of AE if AC = 7 cm.
   b Write down the size of angle CED if angle ACB = 70°.
   c Name an isosceles triangle in the diagram.
   d Name two triangles in the diagram which are congruent to each other. *(MEG)*

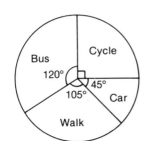

18 The pie chart on the left shows how the 24 pupils in a class travelled to school.
   a How many of these pupils came to school by bus?
   b What fraction of the class travelled by car? Write your answer as simply as possible. *(MEG)*

19 In the diagram below, AB and AC are chords of a circle and AB = AC. The diameter AD meets the chord BC at M, and angle ACM = 62°.
   a (i) Write down the size of angle ABD.
      (ii) Calculate the size of angle DBM.
   b Given that BM = MC = 5 cm, calculate correct to one decimal place
      (i) the length of AM,
      (ii) the length of AB. *(MEG)*

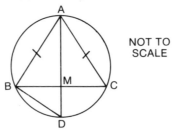

Answers to Exercises

Everyday Arithmetic

Exercise 1A

1 **a** £82; **b** £7 **2** **a** 8500; **b** 2700 **3** £6.03 **4** **a** £5.10; **b** £8, £6.80 **5** **a** 14; **b** 6, 15
6 **a** 328 miles; **b** 7 **7** **a** £1.28; **b** £3; **c** £4.92 **8** Mr Murphy **9** **a** 54; **b** 2 **10** **a** £38;
b £10.25; **c** £2.25 **11** **a** £63.60; **b** 15 **12a** 17p, 23; **b** 11p; **c** 2 × 11p, 6 × 13p; 5 × 11p,
3 × 15p; 6 × 11p, 2 × 17p; 1 × 15p, 5 × 17p

Exercise 1B

1 68 **2** 120 bags **3** 15, 5p **4** £3.04 **5** **a** 16 lengths, £4.80, 80p, £1.60; **b** 5
6 **a** 1710 metres; **b** 14 **7** £27 **8** £22.92, £29.55, £17.90, £25.48, £1.80, £97.65 **9** **a** £58.80;
b 2½ hours **10** **a** 17, 6 packs; **b** 1 × 6, 3 × 17; 2 × 6, 5 × 9; 2 × 6, 3 × 15; 5 × 6, 3 × 9;
7 × 6, 1 × 15; 8 × 6, 1 × 9; 3 × 9, 2 × 15 **11** **a** £2400; **b** £6720; **c** 25 **12** **a** £12.10; **b** £81

Numbers

Exercise 2A

1 7059, less **2** **a** 4210; **b** 2069; **c** 203; **d** 4924 **3** 9°C **4** **a** 8, 5, 7; **b** 9, 6; **c** 5, 2, 3, 9;
d 6, 5, 7, 5 **5** **a** 11301; **b** 1860: **c** 2003 **6** **a** £170; **b** £35 **7** 9, 2; **b** 4, 9; **c** 7, 3; **d** 7, 6
8 **a** 5; **b** −4; **c** −5; **d** 8; **e** 4; **f** −6 **9** **a** 2709: **b** 500 000: **c** 92978; **d** 604 037;
e 604 037, 2709; **f** 601 328 **10** **a** is less than; **b** is greater than; **c** is greater than; **d** is less than
11 **a** −11, −8, −3, −1, 0, 1, 5; **b** 16; **c** −1 **12** **a** 90 feet below sea level: **b** 220 feet;
c 280 feet below sea level **13** 1 035 017, less **14** **a** −3; **b** −17; **c** −2; **d** −4 **15** 60p
16 **a** rise of 9°C; **b** rise of 4°C; **c** fall of 30°F; **d** fall of 6°C; **e** rise of 34°F; **f** fall of 15°F.

Exercise 2B

1 10 201, greater **2** **a** 4°C, −4°C; **b** 7°C; **c** 6 a.m. to 8 a.m. **3** **a** 502; **b** 2903; **c** 1008; **d** 109
4 **a** 8, 3, 6, 7; **b** 1, 5, 5, 7; **c** 1, 4, 2, 8; **d** 2, 4, 1 **5** Business A, £15 000 **6** **a** 3; **b** −7;
c −20; **d** −19 **7** **a** 200 094; **b** 200 104 **8** **a** Tabitha; **b** Samantha's; **c** Samantha; **d** Tabitha
9 **a** 2; **b** −18 **10** **a** 5; **b** 8: **c** 9; **d** 15 **11** £340 **12** **a** is greater than; **b** is less than;
c is greater than **13** 750 000, greater **14** **a** 8 km due south; **b** 12 miles due south;
c 45 miles due north; **d** 1 km due south: **15** −6 **16** **a** fall of 16°C; **b** fall of 9°F; **c** rise of 20°C;
d fall of 13°C: **e** rise of 2°F; **f** fall of 12°F

Exercise 3A

1 **a** <: **b** >; **c** >; **d** > **2** **a** 8; **b** 22; **c** ½; **d** 12 **3** **a** $x \geqslant 5$; **b** $y \leqslant 8$; **c** $w \geqslant 6$; **d** $z \geqslant t$
4 **a** $0 < v < 20$; **b** $8 < s < 15$; **c** $2 < x \leqslant 12$; **d** $0 < z \leqslant 40$; **e** $-10 \leqslant w \leqslant 0$ **5** **a** $2 \times (5-3) = 4$;
b $(10-2) \times 5 = 40$; **c** $(24 \div 6) \div 2 = 2$; **d** $12 - (8 - 10 + 6) = 8$; **e** $8 + (3 \times 4) - 5 = 15$;
f $(12-6) \div (3-1) = 3$ **6** **a** $E > £50$; **b** $E \leqslant £75$: **c** $E \geqslant £300$; **d** $£30 < E < £60$ **7** **a** 27; **b** 37;
c 42

Exercise 3B

1 **a** >; **b** <; **c** >; **d** < **2** **a** 3; **b** 35; **c** 3; **d** 16 **3** **a** $p \leqslant 20$; **b** $r \geqslant s$; **c** $y \geqslant 150$;

d $w \le z$ **4** **a** $14 - (6 \div 2) = 11$; **b** $12 - (8 + 1 - 3) = 6$; **c** $(40 \div 8) \div 2 = 2\frac{1}{2}$; **d** $(7 - 5) \times (6 + 1) = 14$; **e** $2 \times (1 - 3 + 2) = 0$; **f** $6 \div (2 + 4) = 4 - (1 + 2)$ **5** **a** $7 < x < 8$; **b** $-10 < y < 0$; **c** $4 \le w \le 12$; **d** $0 \le z < 12$ **6** **a** $c > p$; **b** $s \ge c$; **c** $p \ge s$; **d** $s < p < c$ **7** **a** 22, 24, 26, 28; **b** 7, 8, 9; **c** $-6, -5, -4, -3$; **d** 8, 9; **e** 6, 12, 18

Exercise 4A

1 **a** 7, 23, 149, 2061; **b** 16, 80, 978 **2** 12, 15, 18, 21, 24 **3** **a** 9; **b** 25; **c** 64 **4** 4, 81, 1, 49 **5** **a** 5, 10, 15, 20, 25, 30; **b** 9, 18, 27; **c** 16 **6** 7, 11, 13, 17, 19 **7** **a** No; **b** Yes; **c** No; **d** Yes; **e** No **8** **a** 8; **b** 125; **c** 1000 **9** **a** 3×5; **b** $2 \times 2 \times 5$; **c** $2 \times 3 \times 7$; **d** $2 \times 2 \times 2 \times 2$; **e** $3 \times 3 \times 11$ **10** 2 **11** No **12** **a** No; **b** Yes; **c** Yes; **d** No; **e** Yes **13** **a** Yes; **b** No; **c** Yes; **d** No; **e** Yes **14** **a** No; **b** No; **c** Yes; **d** No; **e** Yes; **f** No **15** **a** 2; **b** 6; **c** 11; **d** 15 **16** 10 cm **17** **a** 7 cm; **b** 12 cm; **c** 14 cm **18** **a** It is even; **b** It is odd **19** 17 **20** 24 **21** **a** True; **b** False (2 is a prime number); **c** False; **d** True; **e** True

Exercise 4B

1 **a** 5; **b** 9; **c** 50 **2** 32, 36, 40, 44, 48 **3** 6, 12, 18, 24. All are multiples of 6. **4** **a** 16; **b** 49; **c** 81; **d** 169 **5** 64, 9, 324 **6** **a** Yes; **b** No; **c** No; **d** Yes; **e** Yes **7** **a** 3×7; **b** $2 \times 3 \times 3$; **c** $2 \times 2 \times 2 \times 5$; **d** $2 \times 2 \times 13$; **e** 5×17; **f** $2 \times 2 \times 3 \times 11$ **8** **a** $3 \times 7 \times 11$; **b** $5 \times 13 \times 17$ **9** **a** 27; **b** 64; **c** 343 **10** 83, 89, 97 **11** **a** Yes; **b** No; **c** Yes; **d** No; **e** Yes **12** 54 **13** 56 **14** **a** 5; **b** 16; **c** 30 **15** 37 **16** 71, 73 **17** 64 **18** **a** True; **b** True; **c** False; **d** True; **e** False; **f** True

Exercise 5A

1 **a** 7, 5, 23; **b** 7, -4, 5, 23, -11 **2** **a** 8; **b** 13 **3** **a** 12, 24, 36; **b** 12 **4** **a** 15; **b** 8; **c** 30; **d** 48 **5** **a** Rational; **b** Irrational; **c** Irrational; **d** Rational; **e** Rational **6** **a** 3, 5; **b** 15 **7** **a** 6; **b** 4; **c** 22; **d** 16 **8** 1 **9** **a** 21; **b** 32 **10** **a** $-15, \sqrt{49}$; **b** $\sqrt{5}, \sqrt[3]{4}$ **11** **a** 120; **b** 45; **c** 72; **d** 84 **12** **a** 8; **b** 15; **c** 27 **13** **a** True; **b** False; **c** True; **d** True

Exercise 5B

1 **a** 29, 104, 71; **b** -2, 29, 104, -14, 71 **2** **a** 20; **b** 0 **3** -1 **4** **a** 6, 12, 18; **b** 2, 7 **5** **a** 15; **b** 24; **c** 220; **d** 36; **e** 132 **6** **a** 5; **b** 1; **c** 13; **d** 6; **e** 17 **7** **a** Rational; **b** Rational; **c** Irrational; **d** Irrational; **e** Rational; **f** Rational **8** **a** $45, \sqrt{16}$; **b** $2\frac{1}{2}, -8$ **9** **a** 5; **b** 7; **c** 2 **10** **a** 120, 5; **b** 32, 4; **c** 180, 12; **d** 330, 11; **e** 570, 19; **f** 286, 1 **11** **a** True; **b** False; **c** False; **d** True; **e** True

Exercise 6A

1 **b** 10, 15, 21 **2** **a** 19, 23, 27; **b** 32, 35, 38; **c** 13, 11, 9 **3** **a** 25, 36, 49; **b** Odd numbers **4** **a** 16, 32; **b** 81, 243; **c** 10, 5 **5** **a** 1990; **b** 1993; **c** 1996 **6** **b** 25, 36; **d** 60, 84 **7** **a** 10; **b** 20, 25; **c** 25; **d** 24 **8** **a** 5, 8, 13, 21, 34, 55; **b** 2, 4 **9** **a** Double and add 1; 63, 127; **b** Multiply by 3 and subtract 2; 82, 244; **c** Multiply by 5 and subtract 3; 157, 782 **10** **a** 3; **b** 6; **c** Triangular numbers **11** **a** 17, 23; **b** 26, 37; **c** 24, 25; **d** 35, 51 **12** $a = 11, b = 60, x = 8, y = 112$

Exercise 6B

1 **a** 25, 29, 33; **b** 3, 0, -3; **c** 29, 36, 43 **2** **b** 7, 9, 11; **c** 22, 28, 34 **3** **a** 11 metres; **b** 85 metres **4** **a** 48, 96; **b** 256, 1024; **c** $25, 12\frac{1}{2}$ **5** 1, 4, 6, 4, 1; 1, 5, 10, 10, 5, 1; 1, 6, 15, 20, 15, 6, 1, **6** **a** 17; **b** 36; **c** 24, 21; **d** 4 **7** **b** Square numbers; **c** 36 **8** **a** 18, 29; **b** 32 256; **c** 2, 0 **9** **a** 123; **b** 3, 4, 11, 116 **10** **a** 2, 6, 12, 20; **b** 30, 42; **c** Each number is twice the

Fractions and Decimals

Exercise 7

1 **a** $\frac{1}{2}$; **b** $\frac{3}{4}$; **c** $\frac{2}{3}$; **d** $\frac{1}{3}$; **e** $\frac{7}{8}$; **f** $\frac{4}{5}$; **g** $\frac{2}{5}$; **h** $\frac{1}{7}$ **2** **a** 0·5; **b** 0·75; **c** 0·3; **d** 0·2; **e** 0·01; **f** 0·17; **g** 0·8; **h** 0·125; **i** 0·625; **j** 0·35   **3** **a** 0·25; **b** 0·6; **c** 0·375; **d** 0·03   **4** **a** $\frac{1}{10}$; **b** $\frac{1}{4}$; **c** $\frac{2}{5}$; **d** $\frac{9}{100}$; **e** $\frac{1}{1000}$; **f** $\frac{3}{20}$; **g** $\frac{7}{8}$ **5** **a** $\frac{3}{4}$; **b** $\frac{2}{5}$; **c** $2\frac{1}{4}$; **d** $\frac{1}{2}$; **e** $\frac{13}{20}$; **f** $5\frac{3}{4}$; **g** $\frac{7}{8}$; **h** $1\frac{7}{24}$; **i** 4; **j** $1\frac{4}{5}$; **k** $13\frac{1}{8}$ **6** **a** 1·5; **b** 11·7; **c** 0·55; **d** 0·47; **e** 5·59; **f** 5·7; **g** 4·03; **h** 0·657; **i** 10·36   **7** **a** $1\frac{1}{3}$; **b** 18; **c** $\frac{2}{7}$; **d** 16; **e** 22; **f** $\frac{2}{5}$; **g** $2\frac{2}{3}$ **8** $2\frac{3}{4}$; **b** $\frac{1}{6}$; **c** $\frac{5}{8}$; **d** $\frac{7}{15}$; **e** $\frac{1}{18}$; **f** $3\frac{1}{4}$; **g** $4\frac{2}{3}$; **h** $2\frac{1}{8}$; **i** $4\frac{5}{9}$ **9** **a** 1·4; **b** 2; **c** 0·18; **d** 0·04; **e** 1·38; **f** 0·0842; **g** 0·042; **h** 0·144   **10** **a** 10; **b** 12; **c** 16; **d** 20; **e** 0·2; **f** 1·2   **11** **a** 0·14; **b** 0·89; **c** 0·18; **d** 0·83; **e** 0·24   **12** **a** $\frac{7}{8}$; **b** $\frac{7}{12}$ **13** **a** $\frac{1}{3}$; **b** $\frac{1}{4}$

Exercise 8A

1 **a** $\frac{1}{3}$; **b** 3; **c** 4   **2** **a** 24; **b** 30   **3** **a** £3.86; **b** £1.54; **c** £10.42   **4** **a** $\frac{1}{2}$; **b** $\frac{1}{3}$; **c** $\frac{3}{4}$; **d** $\frac{3}{4}$ **5** **a** 50p; **b** £1; **c** £2.25; **d** $\frac{1}{4}$ **6** **a** $\frac{1}{3}$; **b** $\frac{2}{5}$; **c** $\frac{3}{4}$ **7** **a** $\frac{7}{8}$; **b** $\frac{1}{8}$; **c** 40p   **8** **a** 36 days; **b** 20 days   **9** **a** 0·4, 0·375, 0·44; **b** Yasmin   **10** **a** 4·44; **b** 14·8; **c** 78·44   **11** **a** 39 cm; **b** 88·56 cm²   **12** **a** $\frac{1}{3}$; **b** $\frac{2}{5}$; **c** $\frac{3}{5}$ **13** £40   **14** **a** 24 miles per hour; **b** 50 minutes; **c** 90 minutes   **15** **a** £300; **b** £75; **c** $\frac{1}{2}$ **16** $5\frac{1}{4}$ lb, $4\frac{2}{3}$ lb; **b** 24 days, 16 lb

Exercise 8B

1 **a** $\frac{1}{2}$; **b** $\frac{3}{8}$; **c** $\frac{2}{3}$; **d** $\frac{4}{5}$ **2** **a** 60 miles; **b** 16 miles   **3** **a** 9; **b** 48   **4** **a** $\frac{1}{2}$; **b** $\frac{1}{10}$; **c** $\frac{2}{5}$; **d** $\frac{13}{15}$ **5** **a** 24 miles; **b** 55   **6** **a** $\frac{2}{5}$; **b** $\frac{1}{5}$; **c** $\frac{3}{5}$ **7** **a** 165; **b** 300; **c** £15.15   **8** **a** $\frac{3}{4}, \frac{1}{4}$; **b** £1.50, £1.80   **9** **a** 14 m; **b** 18 m   **10** **a** 0·34, 0·35, 0·32; **b** Mrs Evans   **11** **a** $\frac{1}{2}$; **b** $\frac{1}{5}$; **c** $\frac{2}{5}$ **12** **a** 25; **b** 30   **13** **a** $\frac{1}{4}$; **b** 52; **c** 260; **d** $\frac{3}{20}$

Percentage

Exercise 9

1 **a** $\frac{1}{2}$; **b** $\frac{1}{10}$; **c** $\frac{43}{100}$; **d** $\frac{1}{4}$; **e** $\frac{3}{50}$; **f** $\frac{1}{3}$; **g** $\frac{3}{4}$; **h** $\frac{1}{20}$; **i** $\frac{7}{25}$; **j** $\frac{2}{5}$; **k** $\frac{13}{20}$; **l** $\frac{21}{25}$; **m** $\frac{1}{8}$; **n** $\frac{3}{40}$; **o** $\frac{3}{8}$ **2** **a** 6; **b** 20; **c** 18; **d** 70; **e** 12; **f** 6; **g** 15; **h** 360   **3** **a** 37%; **b** 20%; **c** 70%; **d** 80%; **e** $66\frac{2}{3}$%; **f** 22%; **g** $3\frac{1}{2}$%; **h** 36%; **i** 85%; **f** $62\frac{1}{2}$; **k** $8\frac{1}{3}$%   **4** **a** 6p; **b** £64; **c** £57.60; **d** 63p; **e** £1.20; **f** £7.35; **g** £1.36; **h** £1.30

Exercise 10A

1 **a** £6.80; **b** £27.20; **c** £1.02   **2** **a** 9; **b** 8   **3** **a** £18 200; **b** £70 200   **4** **a** 34p; **b** £5.10; **c** 20%   **5** **a** £49.60, £7.44, £57.04   **6** **a** 25%; **b** 54   **7** **a** £5.76; **b** £4.08; **c** £52.08   **8** **a** £1400; **b** £4200; **c** £3360; **d** 40%   **9** **a** 50%; **b** 20%; **c** 30%; **d** 60%   **10** **a** £63; **b** £11.31; **c** £290.25   **11** **a** £40; **b** £46   **12** **a** £756; **b** £219.24; **c** £536.76

Exercise 10B

1 **a** 12; **b** 6   **2** **a** £2790; **b** £3410   **3** **a** 20%; **b** 6 minutes   **4** **a** £34.80; **b** £8.70; **c** £26.10; **d** £45.15   **5** **a** £1980; **b** £165   **6** **a** 120; **b** 12%; **c** 22; **d** 902   **7** **a** 369; **b** 304; **c** 377   **8** **a** £80.50; **b** £966   **9** **a** 119; **b** 91; **c** 40%   **10** **a** £27.84; **b** £201.84; **c** £33.64   **11** **a** 40%; **b** £35 000; **c** £15 000; **d** 75%   **12** **a** £1680; **b** £12 320; **c** £3572.80; **d** £8747.20

Exercise 11

1 **a** 30%; **b** 52%; **c** 8%; **d** 13.7% **2** **a** 71%; **b** 15%; **c** 78%; **d** 24% **3** **a** 143; **b** 465;
c 35; **d** 68; **e** 754; **f** 252; **g** 55; **h** 114 **4** **a** 20%; **b** 10%; **c** 4%; **d** 15%; **e** 25%; **f** 80%;
g $33\frac{1}{3}$%; **h** 35%; **i** 88% **5** **a** 25% gain; **b** 10% gain; **c** 40% loss; **d** 7% loss; **e** 15% loss;
f 35% gain; **g** 24% gain **6** **a** £2.10; **b** £4.20; **c** £6.50; **d** £11.73; **e** £4403; **f** £10.67
7 **a** 50%; **b** 5%; **c** $2\frac{1}{2}$%; **d** 15%; **e** 52%; **f** 64% **8** **a** £48; **b** £2.50; **c** £560; **d** £12 200;
e 80p; **f** £5.25

Exercise 12A

1 **a** 70%; **b** 18 090 **2** **a** 24%; **b** £6783 **3** **a** £110.40; **b** £35.64; **c** £146.04 **4** 21%
5 **a** 71%; **b** 57%; **c** 20%; **d** 50% **6** **a** 19; **b** £8.96; **c** 48p **7** **a** $12\frac{1}{2}$%; **b** £9.18; **c** £311.40;
d £10.38; **e** £18.60; **f** 6% **8** **a** £5.10; **b** £23.80; **c** £308.90; **d** £44.40; **e** £3.60 **9** **a** £26.03;
b £440; **c** £7.60 **10** **a** 7%; **b** £84.10; **c** £83

Exercise 12B

1 **a** 62%; **b** 34 **2** **a** £4.50; **b** £8.25; **c** 55% **3** **a** 6%; **b** 12% **4** **a** 40%; **b** 25%; **c** £8.80;
d £11.60; **e** 32% **5** **a** 25%; **b** 15%; **c** 50%; **d** 45% **6** **a** £1250; **b** £230; **c** 3% **7** **a** £8.75,
£26.55, £3.98, £30.53; **b** 29%; **c** 196; **d** £31.74; **e** 4% **8** **a** £14 910; **b** 7% **9** **a** £6216;
b £12 000 **10** **a** £960; **b** £48 000

Units, Measurement, Estimation

Exercise 13

1 **a** 200 g; **b** 1·4 g; **c** 850 g; **d** 12 700 g; **e** 53.4 g **2** **a** 500 cm; **b** 3·7 cm; **c** 64 cm; **d** 50 000 cm;
e 83·5 cm **3** **a** 8·5 kg; **b** 0·4 kg; **c** 2000 kg; **d** 38 400 kg; **e** 15·2 kg **4** **a** 700 cl; **b** 43 cl; **c** 62 cl;
d 2·3 cl **5** **a** 4·36 m; **b** 7000 m; **c** 2·4 m; **d** 0.39 m; **e** 820 m **6** **a** 8 t; **b** 0·73 t; **c** 0·067 t;
d 57·62 t **7** **a** 1500 ml; **b** 60 ml; **c** 450 ml; **d** 4·7 ml **8** **a** 2 cm; **b** 38 cm; **c** 6 cm; **d** 12 cm
9 **a** 49 kg; **b** 1 kg; **c** 3 kg; **d** 4 kg; **e** 58 kg **10** **a** 14 m; **b** 438 m; **c** 2 m; **d** 33 m; **e** 74 m
11 **a** 70; **b** 680; **c** 100; **d** 30; **e** 140 **12** **a** 700; **b** 5500; **c** 1600; **d** 32 600; **e** 9600

Exercise 14A

1 **a** metres; **b** kilometres; **c** centimetres; **d** millimetres; **e** metres **2** **a** 6 kg; **b** 20 mg; **c** 70 g;
d 1·5 g; **e** 0·8 kg **3** 10 cm **4** **a** 10.15 kg; **b** 10 150 g; **c** 250 **5** **a** 1·4 m; **b** 160 cm; **c** 20 cm
6 **a** 80 cl; **b** 700 ml **7** **a** 44 g; **b** 23 **8** 350 cm **9** 250 g **10** **a** 0.05 mm; **b** 2 mm **11** **a** 66;
b 2 ml **12** **a** 560 km; **b** 150 miles **13** $2\frac{1}{2}$ m **14** **a** 75 g; **b** 66; **c** 105 ml

Exercise 14B

1 **a** grams; **b** tonnes; **c** kilograms; **d** milligrams; **e** tonnes; **f** grams **2** 1000 cl **3** **a** 12 cm;
b 18 cm **4** **a** 7·72 t; **b** 17 280 kg **5** 32 mm **6** 16 **7** **a** 6 feet 6 inches; **b** 13 feet; **c** 26 feet
8 **a** 1300 g; **b** 12 **9** 5·145 kg **10** **a** 12; **b** 45 cm **11** **a** 164 litres; **b** 36 gallons **12** **a** 630 m;
b 8 **13** **a** 0·3 mm; **b** 126

Exercise 15A

1 **a** 5·34; **b** 0·82; **c** 12·08; **d** 1·30 **2** **a** 9·2; **b** 17.3; **c** 0.8; **d** 8·7 **3** **a** 850; **b** 0·032;
c 1100; **d** 0·60; **e** 150 000 **4** **a** 6·23; **b** 12 500; **c** 0·005 01; **d** 20·1; **e** 6300 **5** **a** 500;

b 0·0006; **c** 30 000 000 **6** **a** 215 000; **b** 210 000; **c** 215 000 **7** **a** 333 m²; **b** 332·53 m²;
c 333 m² **8** **a** 525; **b** 534 **9** **a** £150, £61, £120; **b** £330; **c** £320; **d** £320 **10** 3·873 m;
b 3·9 m **11** **a** 122·0 miles; **b** 122 miles; **c** 100 miles **12** 82·86 g **13** **a** 0.051 mm;
b 0·0509 mm

1 **a** 0·6; **b** 12·3; **c** 5·6; **d** 28·5 **2** **a** 4·85; **b** 0·90; **c** 17·36; **d** 2·33 **3** **a** 29; **b** 160;
c 12 000; **d** 0·0053; **e** 650 000 **4** **a** 12·46; **b** 0·4021; **c** 160·1; **d** 0·040 72; **e** 54 240 000
5 **a** 12 700 km; **b** 13 000 km; **c** 13 000 km **6** **a** 11 350; **b** 11 449 **7** **a** 0.0264 g; **b** 0·026 g;
c 0·026 g **8** **a** 0·654 m; **b** 0·7 m; **c** 0·7 m **9** **a** £120; **b** £3400; **c** £3276; **d** £3300; **e** £3300
10 **a** 5; **b** 3; **c** 2 **11** **a** 3·142; **b** 3·1416; **c** 3·141 59 **12** 328.57 ml **13** **a** 4·30 cm;
b 4·3014 cm

Indices, Standard Form

1 **a** 9; **b** $\frac{1}{9}$; **c** 8; **d** $\frac{1}{8}$; **e** 625; **f** $\frac{1}{625}$; **g** $\frac{1}{49}$; **h** $\frac{1}{32}$; **i** $\frac{1}{216}$ **2** **a** 16; **b** 81; **c** $1\frac{1}{2}$; **d** $\frac{4}{5}$; **e** $2\frac{1}{4}$
3 **a** 4; **b** 25; **c** 400; **d** $1\frac{1}{9}$; **e** 625 **4** **a** 42·3; **b** 70·8; **c** 62 000; **d** 4·6; **e** 0·0297; **f** 5; **g** 0·07;
h 0·0049; **i** 0·064 23; **j** 0·000 037 **5** **a** Move the decimal point n places to the right; **b** move the decimal
point n places to the left **6** **a** 8.57×10^2; **b** 2.4×10^{-1}; **c** 5.41×10^{-4}; **d** 2.36×10^5; **e** 7.2×10^7;
f 9×10^{-6} **7** **a** 3×10^{-3}; **b** 1.04×10^6; **c** 4.9×10^{-3}; **d** 2.3×10^{-2}; **e** 2×10^3; **f** 5×10^{-5};
g 2.5×10^2 **8** **a** 2^8; **b** 2^{12}; **c** 2^{x+y}; **d** 2^7; **e** 2^{-5}; **f** 2^{x-y}; **g** 2^8; **h** 2^{-6} **9** **a** 5^3; **b** 5^{-2};
c 5^{-5}; **d** 5^{-6x} **10** **a** 3^6; **b** 3^{20}; **c** 3^{xy}; **d** 3^8; **e** 3^{15}; **f** 3^{18}; **g** 3^6; **h** 3^{-11}

1 **a** 49; **b** $\frac{1}{49}$; **c** $\frac{1}{64}$; **d** $\frac{1}{1000}$; **e** $\frac{1}{81}$ **2** **a** 9; **b** 16; **c** $2\frac{1}{2}$; **d** $\frac{9}{11}$; **e** $1\frac{7}{9}$ **3** **a** 10; **b** 16; **c** $1\frac{2}{3}$; **d** 2500;
e 8000 **4** **a** 27; **b** 6.9; **c** 58 000; **d** 0·3; **e** 8·2; **f** 0·000 72 **5** **a** 9.65×10^3; **b** 5.3×10^{-2};
c 2.5×10^5; **d** 2×10^{-5}; **e** 4.684×10^6 **6** **a** 6×10^{-5}; **b** 8×10^2; **c** 2.8×10^7; **d** 3×10^{-3};
e 4×10^{-6}; **f** 6×10^3 **7** **a** 3^{13}; **b** 3^2; **c** 3^{7x}; **d** 3^{5a}; **e** 3^4; **f** 3^{-9} **8** 7^4; **b** 7^{-2}; **c** 7^{-11};
d 7^{2x} **9** **a** 2^8; **b** 2^{5x}; **c** 2^9; **d** 2^{14}; **e** 2^{15}; **f** 2^{24}; **g** 2^{14}; **h** 2^{-15}

Time

1 **a** 05.00; **b** 16.00; **c** 11.24; **d** 21.05; **e** 14.25; **f** 10.02 **2** **a** 8.20 a.m.; **b** 5 p.m.; **c** 10.06 a.m.;
d 11.45 p.m.; **e** 4.30 p.m.; **f** 11.30 p.m. **3** **a** 35 min; **b** $4\frac{1}{2}$ h; **c** 3 h 55 min **4** **a** 10;
b 31 March 1985 **5** **a** 45 min; **b** 48 min; **c** 12 min; **d** 26 min; **e** 16.19, 49 min; **f** 13 min
6 **a** Sunday; **b** 8 days and 14 hours **7** 7 h 35 min **8** **a** 16.13; **b** 38 min **9** **a** 2 h 30 min;
b 6.35 p.m.; **c** 6 h 30 min; **d** 5 May

1 **a** 02.30; **b** 19.00; **c** 04.26; **d** 23.08; **e** 13.50; **f** 12.30 **2** **a** 3 p.m.; **b** 10.14 a.m.; **c** 9.17 p.m.;
d 4·07 a.m. **e** 10.20 a.m.; **f** 4.30 p.m. **3** **a** 6 h 50 min; **b** $1\frac{1}{2}$ h; **c** 5 h 20 min **4** **a** Sunday;
b Wednesday; **c** Friday; **d** Tuesday **5** **a** 17 min; **b** 2 min, 18 min; **c** 16.03; **d** 16.07; **e** 48 min
6 **a** 16 min 22 s; **b** 3 min 38 s **7** **a** 1973; **b** 12 October; **c** 12 years 2 weeks **8** **a** 1 h 55 min;
b 20 min **9** **a** $8\frac{1}{2}$ h; **b** 48 min **10** **a** 6; **b** 5; **c** 13; **d** Wednesday 3 December

Ratio and Proportion

1 **a** 1:2; **b** 2:3; **c** 4:3; **d** 5:2; **e** 2:5; **f** 1:3:5; **g** 3:4:7; **h** 4:5:20; **i** 1:4; **j** 3:1; **k** 2:5; **l** 9:2
2 **a** $2\frac{1}{2}$ buckets; **b** 18 litres; **c** 5 pots **3** **a** 5:3; **b** 30 **4** **a** 3 onions, 6 oz mushrooms,
$4\frac{1}{2}$ tablespoons flour, $2\frac{1}{4}$ lb chuck steak; **b** $4\frac{1}{2}$ lb; **c** 1 **5** **a** 20 min; **b** 30 min; **c** 4 h; **d** 18 h
6 **a** 0·4 km; **b** 4·8 km; **c** 1·28 km; **d** $17\frac{1}{2}$ cm, **7** **a** Yes; **b** 4p, 12p, 16p, 24p **8** **a** 36 min;
b 3 h 36 min; **c** 1 h 48 min **9** **a** 4 m; **b** 120 cm **10** **a** Direct; **b** Neither; **c** Inverse; **d** Neither;
e Direct; **f** Inverse **11** **a** £2; **b** £8; **c** £1.60; **d** £26.40; **e** £2.20; **f** £5.28 **12** **a** 2·6 cm, 3·6 cm;
b 3 cm; **c** $1\frac{3}{4}$ kg

1 **a** 1:3; **b** 3:2; **c** 5:11; **d** 3:5; **e** 1:3:4; **f** 5:3:2; **g** 7:10; **h** 5:4; **i** 30:1 **2** **a** 55 g; **b** 20 kg;
c 6 kg **3** **a** 3:4; **b** 5:6; **c** 45 **4** **a** 20 oz, 10 oz, 15 oz; **b** $1\frac{1}{3}$ oz; **c** 54, 27 oz **5** **a** 310 miles;
b 6·4 inches; **c** 360 miles **6** **a** £12; **b** £200; **c** £600 **7** 300, 450, 750, 900 **8** **a** 30 min;
b 360 min; **c** 20 min **9** **a** £60; **b** £975; **c** £17 500 **10** **a** 2:15; **b** 63·75 cm; **c** 24 cm 8 mm
11 **a** Neither; **b** Inverse; **c** Inverse; **d** Direct; **e** Neither; **f** Neither **12** **a** 6; **b** 36; **c** 16;
d 72 min

1 **a** £12; **b** £24, £36 **2** £15, £30 **3** **a** 3, 9; **b** 15, 10; **c** 12, 9; **d** 4, 8, 8; **e** 14, 7, 21;
f 40, 24, 16 **4** **a** $\frac{1}{6}$; **b** $\frac{5}{6}$; **c** 35 h **5** **a** $\frac{1}{4}$; **b** $\frac{1}{6}$; **c** 18 min; **d** 63 min; **e** 2 h 10 min; **f** 1 h
6 **a** 75 kg; **b** 24 kg **7** 80p, £1.28, £1.92 **8** **a** 15, 10, 20; **b** 12, 11, 22

1 **a** $\frac{1}{4}$; **b** £5000, £15 000 **2** £5, £25 **3** **a** 16, 8; **b** 15, 25; **c** £1.50, 60p; **d** 22p, 44p, 66p;
e 32, 24, 40; **f** 9, 18, 27 **4** 180 miles **5** **a** 5:6:4; **b** £1000, £1200, £800 **6** **a** 1:2; **b** 3:1:2;
c 20 **7** $16\frac{1}{2}$ miles **8** 140 **9** **a** 22 750; **b** 300, 100, 200, 50

Rate

1 **a** £2.25; **b** £12.15 **2** **a** 12; **b** 304 **3** **a** £600; **b** £1275; **c** £3900; **d** 4 weeks; **e** 14 weeks;
f 29 weeks **4** **a** 30 m; **b** 900 m; **c** 2·7 km; **d** 16 s; **e** 6 min 20 s; **f** 33 min 20 s **5** **a** 37; **b** 211
6 27 700; **b** 132 days **7** **a** 65 words per minute; **b** 975; **c** 24 min **8** **a** 25 853; **b** £3.96
9 **a** 35 m/s; **b** 63 km **10** **a** 33 litres per minute; **b** 4 min 13 s **11** 19 miles **12** **a** 60; **b** 5100;
c 18 **13** **a** 270 miles; **b** 5 hours; **c** 54 miles per hour

1 **a** 420; **b** 23 **2** **a** 46 km/h; **b** 345 km **3** **a** 56; **b** 30 **4** 10 min **5** **a** 9·4; **b** 13
6 **a** 300 m; **b** 18 000 m; **c** 18 km/h; **d** 16·5 km **7** **a** 562·5 kg, 325 kg; **b** 840, 109·2 kg
8 **a** 2·4 dollars per pound; **b** 1032 dollars; **c** £208.33 **9** 18 min 36 s **10** **a** £42;
b Winter, upper gallery; **c** Lower gallery **11** **a** 780 m; **b** 2·6 m/s **12** 1400; **b** 3 weeks and 3 days;
c £89.60; **d** 20 h

Graphs

Exercise 21A

1 **a** 52 cm; **b** 2nd; **c** 94 cm; **d** 23rd; **e** 26 days **2** **a** 37 kg; **b** 18 lb; **c** 29 kg; **d** 48 lb
3 **a** 72 days; **b** 27 **4** **a** 20 min, 15 min; **b** 25 miles; **c** 75 mph; **d** 16.20; **e** 50 mph; **f** 2 h 45 min
5 **a** 38 francs; **b** £2.10 **6** **a** 44 miles per gallon, 45 mph; **b** 22 mph, 66 mph **7** **a** Line A: car,
60 km/h; line B: cyclist, 30 km/h; line C: runner, 18 km/h; **b** 27 min; **c** 7 km; **d** 32 min, 16 km **8** **a** £53;
b 90 miles; **c** £30; **d** 20p; **e** 100 miles **9** **a** 320 g; **b** 580; **c** 30 g **10** **a** 1983; **b** 1981;
c 10 000; **d** 14 400; **e** 8000 **11** **a** Denise, 30 min; **b** 3.21 p.m.; **c** 45 min; **d** 5 km; **e** 50 km/h;
f 5 km/h

Exercise 21B

1 **a** 7 h; **b** 22°C; **c** −3°C; **d** 12.40 a.m., 7.20 a.m.; **e** 48 min; **f** 8°C **2** **a** 91 cm; **b** 21 inches;
c 112 cm/s **3** **a** 3.2 km; **b** 8 min; **c** 4.43 p.m.; **d** 15 min; **e** 8 km/h; **f** 9.6 km/h **4** **a** 180; **b** £160;
c 60 **5** **a** 53 kroner; **b** 33 marks **6** **a** 1180, 260 min; **b** 120 min, 510 min; **c** 350; **d** 160 min
7 **a** 16.40; **b** 60 km/h; **c** 1 h; **d** 14.48, 15.28 **8** **a** £6.40; **b** 24; **c** £1.60; **d** 30p; **e** 7; **f** £3.60
9 **a** 20 s; **b** 27 s; **c** 12 m/s; **d** 40 m/s; **e** 340 m; **f** 240 m **10** **a** 105 g; **b** 42; **c** 14 g; **d** 1.2 g
11 Order of graphs is **e, f, c, b, d, a**

Exercise 22A

1 **a** $(-1.5, 0)$; **b** 2; **c** 2.8; **d** −3; **e** (1.4, 5.8); **f** $x = 1.4, y = 5.8$ **2** **a** 160 km, 290 km, 340 km;
b 50 km; **c** 85, speed in km/h; **d** $d = 85t + 50$ **3** **a** (3, 0), (0, 6); **b** (−6, 0), (0, 4); **c** (6, 0), (0, 1.5);
d (−2.5, 0), (0, 5); **e** (0.3, 0), (0, 0.6) **4** **a** 3.9; **b** 1.7, −1.7; **c** $0.9 < x < 1.3$; **d** 1.7 **5** $x = 3.5$,
$y = 2.5$ **6** **a** 5.9 m; **b** $1.5 < x < 2.4$; **c** 3.2; **d** $y = x$ **7** **a** 2.1 h, 16.5 litres; **b** 26.5 litres, 23.25 litres;
c 1.25 h **8** **a** −3.5; **b** 4.7, −0.7; **c** −4; **d** $x = 2$ **9** **a** $\frac{1}{2}$, rate of growth in cm/day; **b** $h = 3 + 2.4t$;
c 2.8 days, 9.4 cm; **d** 2 days **10** **a** 5, 1.6, −0.8; **b** (−1.4, 7), (1.4, 7); **c** 1.4; **d** (2.54, 2.54)

Exercise 22B

1 **a** −1; **b** $x + y = 2$; **c** 1.5; **d** $x = -1.8, y = -0.2$ **2** **a** 36 m, 48 m; **b** 25 m; **c** 1.8, speed in m/s;
d $d = 1.8t + 25$; **e** −2.2; **f** $d = -2.2t + 57$; **g** 8 s, 39.4 m **3** **a** (12, 0), (0. 4); **b** (2, 0), (0, −4);
c (−1.5, 0), (0, 9); **d** (0.25, 0), (0, 0.5); **e** (0.4, 0), (0, −0.2) **4** **a** 12.1 m³; **b** 1.67; **c** $2 \leq x \leq 2.8$
5 $x = 1.6, y = 3.8$ **6** **a** 104 million; **b** 3.6 years; **c** 116 million; **d** 6 million per year **7** **a** 2.29;
b 0.27, 3.73; **c** 2; **d** −3 **8** **a** 3.6 s; **b** 1.5, rate of gain of speed, or acceleration; **c** $v = 14 - 3t/4$;
d 3.1 s **9** **a** 56.25 cm²; **b** 34.2 cm²; **c** 4.6, 10.4; **d** $3.5 \leq x \leq 11.5$

Statistics

Exercise 23A

1 **a** Best day Wednesday, worst Monday; **b** Pictogram has 3 diagrams, 2 diagrams, 3 diagrams,
4 diagrams; **c** 85; **d** 17 **2** **a** 12, 22, 28, 15, 8; **b** Football; **c** $\frac{1}{4}$; **d** $\frac{3}{20}$; **e** 1250 **3** **a** 32; **b** 82
4 **a** 1; **b** 1; **c** 21; **d** $1\frac{2}{5}$; **e** 4 **5** **a** Frequencies are 7, 9, 6, 6; **c** 6; **d** $\frac{1}{10}$; **e** $\frac{1}{8}$; **f** $\frac{3}{20}$ **6** **a** 30;
b 15; **c** 10; **d** 5; **e** Train **7** 3, 4, 4, 6 **8** **a** 26, 28; **b** Friday, cheese; **c** 140; **d** 28
9 1250, 1000, 1750, 1000; **b** 5000; **c** 1250 **10** 22 **11** 36 **12** **a** Frequencies are 2, 10, 6, 4, 3,
5; **c** 101–200; **d** $\frac{1}{5}$; **e** $\frac{2}{15}$ **13** **a** 15; **b** 10; **c** 25; **d** 120°; **e** 10

Exercise 23B

1 a Pictogram has 7 diagrams, 9 diagrams, 7 diagrams, 6 diagrams; b 1984; c 149; d 1750; e 350
2 a £26, £8, £12, £20; b £120; c $\frac{1}{10}$; d $\frac{1}{6}$; e $\frac{1}{15}$ 3 a 12°C; b $3\frac{1}{2}$°C 4 a 33 min; b 32 min; c 32 min; d 5 min 5 a Frequencies are 2, 5, 6, 4, 3, 2, 3; c 32; d $\frac{1}{8}$; e $\frac{3}{16}$; f 100; g 150 6 a 240; b 200; c 180; d 280 7 11, 12, 14, 17 8 a 15, 21, 16; b 68; c 17; d $3\frac{1}{2}$ 9 a 480, 720, 1200, 360, 480; b 3240; c 648; d 840 10 45 11 a £28; b £42; c £70; d £7 12 a Frequencies are 1, 4, 5, 9, 8, 6, 3; c 36; d $\frac{1}{4}$; e $\frac{2}{9}$; f 476 13 a 30; b 20; c 10; d 72°; e 36

Exercise 24A

1 144°, 90°, 72°, 54° 2 2, 1, $1\frac{1}{3}$ 3 b 11°C–13°C; c 16; d $\frac{3}{8}$ 4 a −1, $\frac{1}{2}$, $1\frac{1}{2}$; b 41, 35, 37 5 a 0; b 1; c 25; d 24; e $\frac{24}{25}$ or 0·96 6 a 0, 1, $1\frac{1}{5}$; b 1. −1, −$1\frac{1}{5}$ 7 94 8 80°, 100°, 110°, 70° 9 a 20 kg–30 kg; b 20; c $19\frac{1}{2}$ kg 10 Median, 2 goals 11 a 5, 8, 6, 4, 2; c 16.5 cm–17·5 cm; d $\frac{2}{5}$; e 17·6 cm 12 a 10; b 10; c $9\frac{1}{2}$; d 182; e 68; f 34

Exercise 24B

1 36°, 108°, 216° 2 50p, £1.10, £1.46 3 b 66 inches–69 inches; c 40; d 70% 4 a 7, 4, 4, 4; b 17, 7, $\frac{1}{2}$, −$\frac{1}{5}$; c 200, 150, 175, $187\frac{1}{2}$ 5 a 3; b 4; c 50; d 189; e 3·78 6 120°, 135°. 45°, 60° 7 a −4, −3, −$2\frac{2}{5}$; b 15, $17\frac{1}{2}$, $19\frac{1}{2}$ 8 28g 9 a 7–8; b 100; c 7·1 10 Mode = 3, median = 4 11 a 4, 8, 6, 2; c 60%; d 10·3 kg 12 38

Probability

Exercise 25A

1 a $\frac{1}{4}$; b $\frac{1}{2}$; c $\frac{3}{4}$ 2 a $\frac{1}{2}$; b $\frac{1}{2}$ 3 a $\frac{1}{5}$; b $\frac{2}{3}$ 4 $\frac{2}{5}$ 5 $\frac{7}{25}$ 6 a $\frac{1}{6}$; b $\frac{1}{2}$; c $\frac{1}{3}$ 7 a $\frac{1}{8}$; b $\frac{3}{8}$; c $\frac{1}{4}$; d $\frac{1}{2}$ 8 $\frac{1}{3}$ 9 a $\frac{1}{7}$; b $\frac{5}{7}$; c $\frac{6}{7}$ 10 a $\frac{1}{25}$; b $\frac{1}{15}$; c $\frac{73}{75}$ 11 a $\frac{1}{5}$; b $\frac{1}{2}$; c $\frac{1}{4}$ 12 a $\frac{1}{5}$; b $\frac{4}{15}$; c $\frac{2}{3}$; d $\frac{13}{15}$ 13 22 14 a $\frac{1}{3}$; b $\frac{1}{2}$ 15 a 8; b $\frac{3}{8}$; c $\frac{1}{4}$

Exercise 25B

1 a $\frac{1}{2}$; b $\frac{1}{3}$; c $\frac{2}{3}$; d $\frac{5}{6}$ 2 $\frac{5}{7}$ 3 a $\frac{2}{3}$; b $\frac{1}{6}$; c $\frac{1}{3}$; d $\frac{1}{4}$; e $\frac{3}{4}$ 4 a $\frac{1}{10}$; b $\frac{1}{5}$; c $\frac{2}{5}$ 5 a $\frac{1}{12}$; b $\frac{1}{3}$; c $\frac{3}{4}$ 6 $\frac{7}{10}$ 7 a $\frac{1}{3}$; b $\frac{1}{6}$; c $\frac{1}{2}$ 8 a $\frac{1}{25}$; b $\frac{2}{25}$ 9 a $\frac{1}{4}$; b $\frac{1}{2}$ 10 a $\frac{1}{4}$; b $\frac{1}{3}$; c $\frac{1}{6}$; d $\frac{5}{12}$ 11 a $\frac{1}{2}$; b $\frac{1}{10}$; c $\frac{3}{10}$; d $\frac{4}{5}$ 12 a $\frac{1}{4}$; b $\frac{1}{5}$; c $\frac{3}{5}$ 13 27 14 a $\frac{2}{9}$; b $\frac{1}{3}$; c $\frac{2}{3}$; d $\frac{5}{9}$ 15 a $\frac{1}{4}$; b $\frac{1}{2}$; c $\frac{1}{4}$

Exercise 26A

1 a $\frac{4}{25}$; b $\frac{9}{25}$; c $\frac{3}{8}$; d $\frac{9}{40}$ 2 a $\frac{1}{24}$; b $\frac{1}{12}$ 3 $\frac{7}{15}$; b $\frac{3}{5}$ 4 a 0·6; b 0·144; c 0·096 5 a $\frac{4}{9}$; b $\frac{1}{9}$; c $\frac{1}{18}$; d $\frac{1}{6}$ 6 $\frac{1}{16}$, $\frac{15}{16}$ 7 a $\frac{2}{5}$; b $\frac{1}{5}$; c $\frac{2}{7}$ 8 a $\frac{6}{7}$; b $\frac{30}{49}$ 9 a $\frac{1}{3}$; b $\frac{1}{3}$; c $\frac{1}{9}$ The game is fair because the players have the same probability of winning. 10 a $\frac{7}{18}$; b $\frac{5}{9}$; c $\frac{1}{6}$ 11 $(1 − x)^2$ 12 a $\frac{8}{27}$; b $\frac{19}{27}$ 13 a $\frac{1}{5}$; b $\frac{1}{5}$; c $\frac{1}{20}$; d $\frac{3}{20}$ 14 a $\frac{5}{9}$; b $\frac{7}{9}$ 15 a $\frac{1}{12}$; b $\frac{1}{2}$; c $\frac{1}{12}$

Exercise 26B

1 a $\frac{1}{2}$; b $\frac{1}{4}$; c $\frac{1}{12}$ 2 a $\frac{13}{24}$; b $\frac{11}{24}$ 3 a $\frac{3}{5}$; b $\frac{2}{5}$ 4 a $\frac{9}{25}$; b $\frac{4}{25}$ 5 a 0·3; b 0·063 6 a $\frac{27}{64}$; b $\frac{37}{64}$ 7 a 0·49; b 0·09; c 0·21; d 0·21; e 0·42 8 a $\frac{2}{7}$; b $\frac{3}{14}$; c $\frac{1}{14}$ 9 a $\frac{1}{6}$; b $\frac{1}{12}$ 10 a $\frac{13}{20}$; b $\frac{2}{5}$ 11 $x^2(1 − x)$ 12 a $\frac{1}{4}$; b $\frac{1}{12}$; c $\frac{1}{6}$ 13 The game is fair because each player's probability of winning is $\frac{1}{4}$ 14 a $\frac{13}{18}$; b $\frac{7}{18}$; c $\frac{11}{18}$

Algebra

1 **a** 17; **b** 28; **c** 3; **d** 20; **e** 7; **f** 40 **2** **a** 55; **b** 36; **c** 0; **d** 27; **e** 8; **f** 10; **g** 16 **3** **a** 12; **b** 6; **c** 7; **d** 3; **e** 5; **f** 6 **4** **a** 16; **b** 121; **c** 18; **d** 100; **e** 144; **f** 8; **g** 49; **h** 20

Exercise 28A

1 **a** £110; **b** £134.40 **2** **a** 80; **b** $D = mN$ **3** **a** 155; **b** 37 **4** **a** 85; **b** 100 min **5** **a** $P = l + 2w$; **b** 44; **c** 45; **d** $= A \bowtie /w$; **e** 462 **6** **a** $p = y - nx$; **b** 12; **c** £4; **d** 8 **7** **a** 10 days; **b** $7\frac{1}{2}$ days **8** **a** £1800; **b** £400; **c** £400; **d** £4800; **e** £25 **9** **a** 20 m; **b** 1·25 m; **c** 51·2 cm **10** **a** $p = 8x$; **b** 120; **c** 20 cm; **d** $A = 3x^2$; **e** 108; **f** 48 cm² **11** **a** 5; **b** 35; **c** 275 **12** **a** 120 cm³; **b** 240 cm³ **13** **a** £40; **b** $W = 16 + 2(N - 50)$ (or $W = 2N - 84$)

Exercise 28B

1 **a** 46; **b** 39 **2** **a** 60; **b** 27 **3** **a** $t = 5x + 8y$; **b** 54; **c** 253 **4** **a** $R = A - 2x$; **b** 16; **c** 43 cm² **5** **a** 10°C; **b** 25°C; **c** −5°C; **d** 7·8°C **6** **a** 16 cm²; **b** 30·25 m² **7** **a** £28; **b** £54; **c** £36.60; **d** £20; **e** 20p **8** **a** 87; **b** 132 m **9** **a** 21; **b** 78; **c** 1540; **d** 420 **10** **a** $x + y$; **b** $2x + 3y$; **c** $(2x + 3y)/(x + y)$; **d** 2·25; **e** 2·56 **11** **a** 20; **b** 72; **c** 342 **12** **a** $M = 10x$; **b** $M = 500 + 20(y - 50)$ (or $M = 20y - 500$) **13** **a** $P = 10x + 2y$; **b** 44 cm; **c** $A = 6x^2 + xy$; **d** 180

Exercise 29A

1 $3x - 2$ **2** $8x - 3y$ **3** $5b - 3a$ **4** $4x - 4p$ **5** $6a + 3b - 9$ **6** $4t - 2s - 2q$ **7** $2x - 5x^2$ **8** $-3ab - 5c$ **9** $7xy + 2x - y$ **10** $pq - 2p^2 - p$ **11** $10x + 6$ **12** $4x + 8y$ **13** $-15a + 9b$ **14** $2x - xy$ **15** $-6ps + 10p$ **16** $15wx - 35wt$ **17** $x^2 + 2xy$ **18** $-12x^2 + 15xy$ **19** $2xy^2 + x^2y - xy$ **20** $10p^2 - 20p + 30p^2q$ **21** $3(x + 2)$ **22** $4(2a + 3b)$ **23** $5(3 + 4p - 5q)$ **24** $7(1 - 2t - 5r)$ **25** $x(4 + y)$ **26** $a(b - 2c + 1)$ **27** $5a(2 - 3b + 4c)$ **28** $x(x + 4)$ **29** $3y(y + 6x)$ **30** $2y(4x - 3y - 5w)$ **31** $3ab(3c + 7 - 5a)$ **32** $5x^2y(1 - 3y + 4z)$ **33** 4 **34** 3 **35** 5 **36** $1\frac{1}{2}$ **37** 1 **38** $1\frac{1}{3}$ **39** −7 **40** $-2\frac{1}{2}$ **41** $2\frac{1}{3}$ **42** 0 **43** $-2\frac{2}{3}$ **44** 6 **45** 15 **46** 7 **47** −1 **48** $-1\frac{1}{3}$ **49** $1\frac{1}{5}$ **50** $-\frac{1}{5}$

Exercise 29B

1 $5a - 1$ **2** $7x - 13y$ **3** $2q + p$ **4** $3r - 5t - 3$ **5** $5a - 4b$ **6** $3p - 2p^2$ **7** $7y - 5xy$ **8** $3ax - xy - ay$ **9** $6x + 15$ **10** $-7x + 21y$ **11** $48a + 30b$ **12** $4p - pq$ **13** $18xy - 6yw$ **14** $-20t^2 - 8tr$ **15** $4ab^2 - 2a^2b - 3ab$ **16** $6y - 7x$ **17** $3a - 2b + 3ab$ **18** $3p - 16q$ **19** $2x + 3y$ **20** $2(x - 5)$ **21** $3(3p + 5q)$ **22** $6(2x - 3y + 4)$ **23** $4(1 - 4r - 5s)$ **24** $x(5 - 2y)$ **25** $2b(a - 2c)$ **26** $7y(2x - 4z + 5y)$ **27** $6ab(1 - 2c + 3a)$ **28** $5xy(4x - 3y + 1)$ **29** 3 **30** 2 **31** 5 **32** 8 **33** −6 **34** $2\frac{1}{3}$ **35** $3\frac{1}{2}$ **36** $\frac{1}{2}$ **37** 2 **38** $-2\frac{1}{2}$ **39** 10 **40** 12 **41** −2 **42** $3\frac{1}{2}$ **43** $1\frac{1}{2}$ **44** $3\frac{1}{3}$ **45** $4\frac{2}{3}$

Exercise 30A

1 **a** $(3x + 4)$ km; **b** 28 **2** **a** £$(2x + 10)$; **b** $x = 8$, cost price = £18, selling price = £24 **3** **a** $(x + 10)$ years, $(x + 7)$ years; **b** $x = 9$, ages are 9 years, 6 years **4** **a** $(18N + 20)$; **b** 10 **5** **a** $p = 50$, angles are 130°, 62°, 32°; **b** $p = 39$, angles are 108°, 51°, 21° **6** **a** $n, n + 2, n + 4, n + 6, n + 8$; **b** 120, 122, 124, 126, 128 **7** **a** £$(x + 100)$, £$(2x + 200)$; **b** $x = 2100$, Mrs Maxwell gets £4400 **8** **a** $(6x + 40)$ m; **b** 340 m; **c** $x = 70$, perimeter = 460 m; **d** $x = 85$, width = 115 m **9** **a** $7y + 80$; **b** 8 **10** **a** $(2x + 18)$ cm, $(7x + 6)$ cm²; **b** 2·4 **11** **a** $x = vt$; **b** $(6v + 10)$ km; **c** 65 **12** **a** $(35 - 3t)$ h; **b** 9 **13** **a** $2x - 1, 4x - 3$; **b** $7x - 4$; **c** 65, 129, 257

1 **a** £2x, £(x − 20); **b** £120, £100; **c** x = 90; amounts earned are £90, £180, £70 **2** **a** 60 − 7x; **b** 7
3 **a** 9; **b** 13; **c** 8 **4** 35, 36, 40 **5** **a** (18n − 18)p; **b** 22 **6** **a** x − 3, x + 3, x + 6; **b** 4x + 6; **c** 32
7 **a** p − 30, 3p − 90; **b** p = 270, dictionary has 720 pages **8** **a** 11; **b** 17 **9** **a** 4; **b** 12 **10** **a** $1\frac{1}{2}$;
b 1·8 **11** $1\frac{1}{2}$ **12** **a** 2 + x, 2 + 2x, 4 + 3x; **b** x = 9; terms are 2, 9, 11, 20, 31

Exercise 31A

1 3 − 2x **2** aw + t **3** p − 2 **4** ax + w − 3 **5** $\dfrac{7}{x}$ **6** $\dfrac{3}{2s}$ **7** $\dfrac{d}{ab}$ **8** $\dfrac{w-4}{a}$ **9** $\dfrac{8-x}{w}$

10 $\dfrac{v-u}{a}$ **11** $\dfrac{m-4x}{2}$ **12** $\dfrac{2+3y-a}{5a}$ **13** $\dfrac{5x+2p-w}{3w}$ **14** $\dfrac{2xy-5}{x}$ **15** $\dfrac{y-2v^2}{6av}$ **16** 5y

17 2wy **18** $6x^2$ **19** $\dfrac{2y}{a}$ **20** $\dfrac{15rt}{2q}$ **21** ms − 2s **22** $\dfrac{2}{x}$ **23** $\dfrac{at}{w}$ **24** $\dfrac{3}{8a}$ **25** $\dfrac{y-xt}{t}$

26 $\dfrac{w-2px}{6p}$ **27** $\dfrac{2s-ut}{t}$ **28** $\dfrac{py+a^2}{a}$ **29** $\dfrac{2t+2x-3a}{3x}$ **30** $\dfrac{a+2r+ay}{a}$

Exercise 31B

1 3 − 5w **2** y + rs **3** 7 − 2t **4** 3m − x − 4 **5** $\dfrac{r}{6}$ **6** $\dfrac{rt}{wx}$ **7** $\dfrac{2m}{5v^2}$ **8** $\dfrac{ws-y}{a}$

9 $\dfrac{4-x}{3a}$ **10** $\dfrac{2-ab+c}{a}$ **11** $\dfrac{x^2y-q}{pq}$ **12** $\dfrac{3-xy}{2x}$ **13** $\dfrac{6y-s}{3yb}$ **14** $\dfrac{xa-4a-12}{x}$ **15** 10a

16 xy^2 **17** $\dfrac{rt}{6x}$ **18** $\dfrac{c^2d^2}{b^2}$ **19** 3r − xr **20** 2x − 10 **21** $\dfrac{4}{3t}$ **22** $\dfrac{m^2}{7}$ **23** $\dfrac{2}{5wy}$

24 $\dfrac{15ax^2}{2p^2}$ **25** $\dfrac{x-ws}{w}$ **26** $\dfrac{a^2t-p}{at}$ **27** $\dfrac{6a-yv}{y}$ **28** $\dfrac{3x+2a}{a}$ **29** $\dfrac{x^2ya-2y}{xy}$

30 $\dfrac{2xp-ax-ay}{2x}$

Mensuration

Exercise 32A

1 **a** Square; **b** Right-angled isosceles triangle; **c** Trapezium; **d** Parallelogram **2** **a** 27 cm; **b** 66 cm;
c 17·5 m; **d** 20·9 m; **e** 37·8 cm **3** **a** 126 m²; **b** 12 cm²; **c** 260 m²; **d** 24 m²; **e** 9·28 cm²
4 **a** 14 cm, 10 cm²; **b** 36 m, 17 m²; **c** 24 cm, 11 cm²; **d** 60 m, 116 m² **5** **a** 27 cm³; **b** 40 cm³;
c 343 m³; **d** 663 m³ **6** **a** 104 cm³; **b** 180 m³ **7** **a** 22 m, 12 m; **b** 264 m²; **c** 200 m²; **d** 64 m²
8 **a** 24 m²; **b** 6 m²; **c** 36 m² **9** **a** 140 m²; **b** 9 cm² **10** **a** 12·56 m; **b** 37·68 m; **c** 32·97 cm
11 **a** 36 m; **b** 126 m **12** **a** 1600; **b** 5900 cm² **13** **a** 8 cm³; **b** 24 cm² **14** **a** 96 cm³, 136 cm²;
b 3 m³, 14 m²

Exercise 32B

1 **a** Rectangle; **b** Rhombus; **c** Isosceles triangle; **d** Trapezium **2** **a** 57 cm; **b** 14 cm; **c** 37·5 cm;

d 54·8 m   **3**   **a** 36 cm²;   **b** 120 m²;   **c** 112·5 m²;   **d** 30 cm²;   **e** 161·5 m²   **4**   **a** 32 m, 40 m²;
b 19·6 m, 21·2 m²;   **c** 42 m, 46 m²   **5**   **a** 100 cm³;   **b** 216 cm³;   **c** 1228.5 cm³   **6**   **a** 8 cm³;   **b** 6;
c 48 cm³;   **d** 22;   **e** 88 cm²   **7**   **a** 6, 12, 8;   **b** 5, 8, 5;   **c** 8, 12, 6   **8**   1360 m²;   **b** 1080 m²;   **c** 280 m²
9   **a** 220 cm;   **b** 264 cm   **10**   **a** 25·12 cm;   **b** 1256 cm   **11**   **a** Rhombus, trapezium;   **b** 4 cm²;   **c** 9 cm²
12   Figures **b** and **e**   **13**   **a** 4 cm²;   **b** 2 cm²;   **c** 12 cm²   **14**   **a** 20 cm²;   **b** 4 cm²;   **c** 1 cm²;   **d** 10 cm²

Exercise 33A

1   **a** 75 m²;   **b** 154 cm²;   **c** 1256 cm²;   **d** 2464 m²   **2**   **a** 60 m²;   **b** 16·5 cm²;   **c** 414 m²   **3**   **a** 13 m²;
b 574 m²   **4**   **a** 120 m²;   **b** 1800 m³   **5**   **a** 512 cm³;   **b** 72 cm³;   **c** 7;   **d** 8 cm³   **6**   900 m²
7   960 cm³;   **b** 16 cm   **8**   **a** 45 m²;   **b** 540 m³   **9**   **a** Triangular prism;   **b** 36 cm³;   **c** 84 cm²
10   0·385 m³

Exercise 33B

1   **a** 192 cm²;   **b** 616 cm²;   **c** 2826 m²;   **d** 2·43 m²   **2**   **a** 330 m²;   **b** 24·5 cm²;   **c** 4 square units;
d 18 square units   **3**   **a** 240 cm²;   **b** 150 cm²;   **c** 90 cm²   **4**   **a** 1824 cm³;   **b** 1767 cm³;   **c** 57 cm³
5   990 cm³   **6**   40·82 cm²   **7**   **a** 38·5 cm²;   **b** 5·2 cm   **8**   **a** 0·9 m²;   **b** 0·72 m³   **9**   **a** 240 cm³;
b 276 cm²   **10**   **a** 150;   **b** 28·26 cm²;   **c** 1161 cm²

Geometry

Exercise 34A

1   35°;   **b** 132°;   **c** 65°;   **d** 146°   **2**   **a** 50°;   **b** 98°;   **c** 125°;   **d** 27°

3

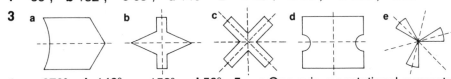

4   **a** 270°;   **b** 140°;   **c** 158°;   **d** 50°   **5**   **a** One axis, no rotational symmetry;   **b** No symmetry;
c Rotational symmetry only;   **d** Two axes and rotational symmetry   **6**   **a** 40°;   **b** 62°;   **c** 19°;   **d** 103°;
e 60°   **7**   **a** 3;   **b** 2;   **c** 4;   **d** 2;   **e** 5   **8**   **a** 45 mm, 90°;   **b** Right-angled isosceles;   **c** 45°
9   **a** 35°, 145°;   **b** 100°, 57°;   **c** 67°, 46°;   **d** 118°, 31°;   **e** 50°, 140°   **10**   **a** 1;   **b** 2;   **c** 1
11   **12**   **a** 40°;   **b** 108°;   **c** 87°;   **d** 80°;   **e** 106°, 94°   **13**   **a** 5, 5;   **b** 8, 8

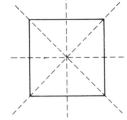

Exercise 34B

1   **a** 20°;   **b** 105°   **2**   **a** 30°;   **b** 150°;   **c** 260°;   **d** 300°   **3**   **a** 100°;   **b** 26°;   **c** 58°;   **d** 65°
4

5   **a** 225°;   **b** 130°;   **c** 120°   **6**   **a** B, W, E;   **b** X, O;   **c** X, N, O   **7**   **a** 70°;   **b** 29°;   **c** 34°;   **d** 133°
8   **a** Yes, order 2;   **b** No;   **c** Yes, order 8;   **d** Yes, order 4;   **e** Yes, order 2;   **f** Yes, order 6
9   **a** 132°, 48°;   **b** 136°, 95°;   **c** 78°, 24°;   **d** 100°, 40°
10   a   b

11   **a** Isosceles trapezium;   **b** (−1, −3), (1, −3);   **c** Symmetrical about *y*-axis, rotational symmetry
of order 2   **12**   **a** 86°;   **b** 112°;   **c** 95°;   **d** 260°

Exercise 35A

1   **a** *b* and *f*;   **b** *a* and *e*, *b* and *d*;   **c** *b* and *c*;   **d** 80°, 80°, 100°   **2**   **a** 35°;   **b** 80°;   **c** 68°;   **d** 55°
3   **a** 360°;   **b** 72°;   **c** 108°   **4**   **a** 140°;   **b** 10;   **c** 15   **5**   **a** 30°;   **b** 60°   **6**   **a** 90°;   **b** 24°;   **c** 90°;
d 66°   **7**   **a** 34°, 146°;   **b** 50°, 30°;   **c** 40°, 25°   **8**   **a** Triangle OAC;   **b** 90°;   **c** 38°
9   **a** AB is a diameter, or AB passes through the centre of the circle, or AB is an axis of symmetry of the
figure;   **b** 90°;   **c** 58°;   **d** 32°   **10**   48°   **11**   **a** 90°, 108°;   **b** 36°;   **c** 18°

Exercise 35B

1   **a** Angle DBF;   **b** Angle BFA;   **c** Angle BDE   **2**   **a** $x = 82°$, $y = 106°$;   **b** $p = 63°$, $q = 43°$;   **c** $r = 28°$,
$s = 36°$ **3**   **a** 45°;   **b** 150°;   **c** 720°;   **d** 20   **4**   **a** 48°;   **b** 128°   **5**   **a** 36°;   **b** 54°;   **c** 126°   **6**   **a** 90°;
b P is the centre of the circle;   **c** Triangles PAC and PBC;   **d** 26°, 64°   **7**   **a** 24°;   **b** 65°, 40°;   **c** 21°, 47°
8   **a** 52°;   **b** 52°   **9**   **a** 15°;   **b** 60°   **10**   **a** 90°;   **b** 34°;   **c** 124°;   **d** 22°   **11**   **a** O is the centre
because the perpendicular bisectors of the chords AC and CE meet at O;   **b** Triangles OBC and OAC;
c 40°, 65°, 25°

Exercise 36A

1   **a** 078°;   **b** 125°;   **c** 270°;   **d** 220°;   **e** 296°   **2**   **a** Hull;   **b** Scarborough;   **c** Scunthorpe;
d Harrogate;   **e** Sheffield   **3**   **a** 9 cm;   **b** 1·8 km;   **c** 102°;   **d** 282°   **4**   **b** 158 m   **5**   **a** 5 cm, 10 miles;
b 38 miles;   **c** 43 miles   **6**   **b** 24 km;   **c** 029°   **7**   28.5 feet   **8**   **a** 150 km;   **b** 960 km;   **c** 042°, 297°
9   32 m, 29 m

Exercise 36B

1   **a** 100°;   **b** 050°;   **c** 242°;   **d** 322°   **2**   **a** Memphis;   **b** New York;   **c** New Orleans;   **d** Chicago;
e Atlanta   **3**   **a** 3·3 cm;   **b** 330 km;   **c** 165 km;   **d** 400 km;   **e** 140°;   **f** 220°   **4**   **a** 26 cm;   **b** 58°
5   **a** 79–85 km;   **b** 87–93 km;   **c** 69–75 km   **6**   **a** 1120 m;   **b** 069°   **7**   **a** 5 m;   **b** 5 m;   **c** 14 m
8   **a** 023°;   **b** 229°;   **c** 322°

Exercise 37A

1   **a** D;   **b** E, H   **2**   **a** P, S;   **b** Y, Z;   **c** K, N   **3**   Triangles ABP, ADP; triangles BCP, DCP; triangles
ABC, ADC   **4**   **a** Triangle AFM;   **b** Quadrilateral FEDM;   **c** quadrilateral AFEB   **5**   **a** Triangle CDF;
b Triangles CEF, FGC   **6**   (5, 5)   **7**   D is (1, 2), E is (3, 0), F is (3, 2)   **8**   **a** Yes;   **b** No;   **c** Yes
9   **a** No;   **b** Yes;   **c** Yes;   **d** No

Exercise 37B

1   **a** Shapes A and F, shapes B, E and H, shapes D and G;   **b** Shape C   **2**   **a** R, T;   **b** X, Z;   **c** K, M

3 Triangles ADP, BCP; triangles CDA, DCB; triangles ABC, BAD **4 a** Triangle AHE; **b** Triangle AFC; **c** Quadrilateral FEDC **5 a** Triangles DCE, CBD; **b** Triangle BCE **6** (2, 2) **7 a** (7, 3); **b** (1, −1), (7, −1) **8 a** No; **b** Yes; **c** No **9 a** Yes; **b** Yes; **c** No; **d** Yes; **e** No

Exercise 38A

1 a 2:1; **b** 2:1; **c** 6 cm **2 a** A square of side 2 cm; **b** (4, 2), (6, 2); **c** (−2, 3), (−2, 6) **3 a** P, R; **b** Y, Z; **c** J, M **4 a** 3; **b** (0, 4) **5 a** Angles ABC, AXY, angles ACB, AYX; **b** 16 cm; **c** 13 cm; **d** 24 cm **6 a** (1, 3), (3, 3), (4, 1); **b** (−4, 0) **7 a** ABCDE, PQRST; **b** 3:1; **c** 15 cm; **d** 8 cm; **e** 14 cm; **f** W, 3 **8 b** (4, 0), (8, 8); **d** (−1, 0), (−1, 4); **e** 2, (−6, 0)

Exercise 38B

1 a B; **b** WX; **c** XL = 10 cm; **d** AB = 10.5 cm **2 b** (3, 3), (9, 3), (3, 6); **d** (4, −2), (12, −2), (4, 2) **3 a** P, S; **b** W, Y; **c** K, M **4 a** 3; **b** (2, 7) **5 a** ABCD, ANML, AFED; **b** 8 cm; **c** 6 cm; **d** A, 2 **6 a** A rhombus; **b** (6, 9), (8, 5), (6, 1); **c** (−2, 7) **7 a** 4; **b** 5 cm; **c** 36 cm **8 a** (4, 2), (4, 4), (0, 4), (2, 2); **b** (8, 4), (8, 8), (0, 8), (4, 4); **c** 4, (8, 0)

Exercise 39A

1 a Reflection in the *y*-axis; **b** Reflection in the *x*-axis; **c** Half-turn about 0; **d** Translation of 5 units downwards; **e** Translation of 8 units to the left **2 a** (−1, 1), (−4, 1), (−4, 2); **b** (−1, −1), (−4, −1), (−4, −2); **c** Reflection in the *x*-axis **3 a** (3, 3); **b** (−2, −2) **4 a** (0, 4), (−1, 4); **b** (5, 5), (5, 1), (6, 1) **5 a** Translation of 1 cm to the right; **b** Reflection in the line MN; **c** Half-turn about the mid-point of AN **6 a** (2, 2), (3, 2), (2, 4); **b** (−2, −2), (−3, −2), (−2, −4); **c** Half-turn about 0 **7** Anticlockwise quarter-turn about 0 **8 a** (4, 5), (6, 5), (6, 4); **b** Translation of 6 units upwards **9 a** (−2, −2), (−5, −2), (−2, −3); **b** (2, −4), (5, −4), (2, −3); **c** Half-turn about the point (0, −3) **10 a** Trapezium CQJO; **b** Triangle BPJ; **c** Trapezium QKOB; **d** Reflection in the line OC; **e** Anticlockwise quarter-turn about O

Exercise 39B

1 a Reflection in the *x*-axis; **b** Translation of 7 units to the right; **c** Half turn about O; **d** Reflection in the *y*-axis; **e** Anticlockwise quarter-turn about O; **f** Clockwise quarter-turn about O **2 a** (0, 4), (1, 3), (2, 4); **b** (0, −4), (−1, −3), (−2, −4); **c** Half-turn about the origin **3 a** (5, 4); **b** (−2, −3) **4 a** (−2, 0), (−6, 0), (−6, −2); **b** (2, 4), (0, 4); **c** (−2, 4), (−4, 4); **d** Translation of 4 units to the left **5 a** Triangles QPO, SRO; **b** Triangle POQ; **c** Triangles PAS, RCQ; **d** Translation of 2 cm to the left and 1 cm upwards; **e** Reflection in the line OR; **f** Reflection in the line SO; **g** Half-turn about the mid-point of SP **6 a** (−3, 2), (1, 4); **b** (0, −3), (−2, −1); **c** Translation of 5 units to the right and 4 units upwards **7 a** (−4, 1), (−4, 2), (−2, 2); **b** (4, 1), (4, 2), (2, 2); **c** Reflection in the *y*-axis **8 a** Translation of 8 cm to the right; **b** Translation of 12 cm to the right; **c** Translation of 2*x* cm to the right **9 a** (−2, 1), (−4, 1), (−2, 0); **b** (−1, 2), (−1, 4), (−2, 2); **c** Anticlockwise quarter-turn about the origin

Trigonometry, Pythagoras' Theorem

Exercise 40

1 a 6·43 cm; **b** 18·5 m; **c** 15·9 cm; **d** 6 m; **e** 16·9 m; **f** 7·13 cm **2 a** 66·4°; **b** 44·4°; **c** 43·2°; **d** 63·4°; **e** 28·0°; **f** 34·8° **3 a** 3·61 m; **b** 10·3 cm; **c** 6 cm; **d** 13·0 m; **e** 191 m; **f** 43·3 cm **4 a** 8·97 cm; **b** 16·5 m; **c** 13·8 m; **d** 24·3 m; **e** 1·46 m; **f** 0·694 cm **5 a** *x* = 5·91 m, θ = 61·7°; **b** *x* = 5·73 m, *y* = 6·28 m; **c** *x* = 20·9 cm, θ = 48·6°; **d** *x* = 86·6 m, *y* = 34·4 m **6 a** 4·36 m; **b** *x* = 8·54 cm, θ = 69·4°; **c** 40·6°; **d** *x* = 21·6 cm, *y* = 8·93 cm; **e** 35·1 m

Exercise 41A

1　**a** 53·9 km;　**b** 112°　2　48·7 m　3　9·06 cm, 181 cm²　4　**a** 72·1 cm;　**b** 112·6°;　**c** 66·6 cm
5　**a** 225 m;　**b** 068°;　**c** 149 m;　**d** 126°;　**e** 151 m　6　118 m　7　**a** 7·78 km;　**b** 3·83 km
8　**a** 9·06 m;　**b** 8·94 m　9　**a** 2·89 m;　**b** 4·20 m;　**c** 1·31 m　10　**a** 60°;　**b** 364 m:　**c** 105 m;
d 1070 m (to 3 s.f.);　**e** 47 700 m² (tp 3 s.f.)

Exercise 41B

1　526 m　2　**a** 11·7 m;　**b** 78·0°　3　20·8 feet　4　249°　5　**a** 3·86 m;　**b** 57·1°;　**c** 21·2 m²
6　Angle AEF = 60° **a** 6 cm;　**b** 10·4 cm;　**c** 31·2 cm²;　**d** 249 cm²;　**e** 374 cm²　7　**a** 130 cm;　**b** 26 cm:
c 1·3 cm;　**d** 6·5 cm　8　44·0°　9　**a** 26·9 km;　**b** 46·6 km;　**c** 305°　10　**a** 33·2 m;　**b** 25·2°;

Answers to GCSE Specimen Papers

Paper 1

1 3100 **2** $\frac{1}{4}$ **3** 4.68 m **4 a** 6 min; **b** 4 min; **c** 2000 m; **d** 2·5 **5** 42 **6 a** 3, 7, 7; **b** 5, 1, 2, 2 **7 a** 12 oz; **b** About $\frac{3}{8}$ of a pint **8** 5 hours **9 a** 16, 19; **b** 96, 192; **c** 36, 49 **10 a** £100; **b** 500; **c** £44

11 a [diagram] **b** [diagram] **12** 64° **13 a** 60 Schillings;

b £1.66 plus or minus 3p; **c** 216 plus or minus 2 **14 a** 5°C; **b** 11°C **15 a** Clacton; **b** ; **b** 340 km; **c** Norwich; **d** 067° **16 a** 1 hr 45 min; **b** Blackpool Holiday Show; **c** 12 June; **d** 5 h **17 b** $\frac{1}{4}$; **c** $\frac{1}{2}$ **b** 3; **d** $\frac{1}{10}$ **e** 3000; **f** 20%

18 a

Age	21–30	31–40	41–50	51–60	61–70	71–80	Over 80
Frequency	4	6	3	3	1	2	2

19 a 1500 m²; **b** 28 m; **c** 116 m²; **d** 30 m²; **e** 100 m³; **f** 110 m²

Paper 2

1 0·088, 0·625, 0·66, 0·667 **2 a** 8; **b** 12; **c** 1 **3** 63° **4 a** 5950 g; **b** 42 g **5 a** 07·50; **b** 07·42 **6** 4 **7** Large. This costs 0·9125 p per gram, Family costs 0·97 p per gram, Standard costs 0·94 p per gram. **8 a** About 8.09 a.m.; **b** 40·5°C; **c** About 10.06 a.m.; **d** About 7 h 20 min; **e** About 7.50 p.m. **9 a** 900; **b** 400 **10 b** 9·7 cm; **c** 485 m; **d** 42°; **e** 122°; **f** 302°; **g** 410 m **11 a** 6·28 ft; **b** 439·6 ft; **c** 400 ft **12 a** £7020; **b** 3900; **c** £35 100; **d** £75 960; **e** £3798; **f** £7371; **g** £4160 **13 a** 5 cm; **b** All sides equal 5 cm; **c** Opposite angles are equal, all 4 angles add up to 360°; **d** Rotational symmetry about (5, 5), line symmetry about PR and QS; **e** 10 cm² **14 a** £6.24; **b** £15; **c** 24p **15 a** £120; **b** 250 km; **c** 225 km **16 a** (i) 13, 49, 109 (ii) 4, 49 (iii) 13, 109; **b** (i) 27 (ii) 33; **c** 148, 193. Differences increase by 6 each time; **d** 94, 127 **17 a** $\frac{1}{2}$ hour; **b** 1$\frac{1}{2}$ hours; **c** 180 km; **d** 2 h; **e** 90 km/h; **f** 1·5

Paper 3

1 a 15 400; **b** 23 950, 24 049 **2 a** 48 m²; **b** 252 m² **3** 9·3 × 10⁷ **4** 155° **5 a** (12, 0); **b** (0, 5); **c** 13 **6 a** 99 km; **b** 15°, 075°; **c** Angles are 90°, 35°, 55°; **d** (i) 16·4 km (ii) 79·4 km **7 a** 20; **b** 7; **c** $a = (v - u)/t$ **8** 64 **9** £112·50 **10 c** 2; **d** −0·73, 2·73 **11 a** 3⁻²; **b** $\frac{1}{9}$ **12 a** (−1, −1), (−5, −1), (−5, −3); **b** (5, −1), (1, −1), (1, 3); **c** (−1, 1), (−5, 1), (−5, 3); **d** Translation of 6 units to the right; **e** Reflection in the x-axis **13 a** 51°; **b** 20·8 **14** Draw 1: $\frac{3}{4}$, $\frac{1}{4}$; draw 2: $\frac{4}{7}$, $\frac{3}{7}$, $\frac{3}{7}$, $\frac{4}{7}$ **15 a** £3x; **b** £500; **c** £1400 **16 a** 1·18 cm; **b** 4·8 cm; **c** 14·4 cm³, 14 400 000 cm³ **17 a** 14 cm; **b** 70°; **c** Triangle ACD or triangle CED; **d** Triangles CAB, CDB **18 a** 8; **b** $\frac{1}{8}$ **19 a** (i) 90° (ii) 28°; **b** (i) 9·4 cm (ii) 10·7 cm